Glencoe Mathematics

Geometry

Chapter 5
Resource Masters

New York, New York   Columbus, Ohio   Chicago, Illinois   Peoria, Illinois   Woodland Hills, California

Consumable Workbooks Many of the worksheets contained in the Chapter Resource Masters are available as consumable workbooks in both English and Spanish.

	ISBN10	ISBN13
Study Guide and Intervention Workbook	0-07-877344-X	978-0-07-877344-0
Skills Practice Workbook	0-07-877346-6	978-0-07-877346-4
Practice Workbook	0-07-877347-4	978-0-07-877347-1
Word Problem Practice Workbook	0-07-877349-0	978-0-07-877349-5
Spanish Versions		
Study Guide and Intervention Workbook	0-07-877345-8	978-0-07-877345-7
Practice Workbook	0-07-877348-2	978-0-07-877348-8

Answers for Workbooks The answers for Chapter 5 of these workbooks can be found in the back of this Chapter Resource Masters booklet.

StudentWorks Plus™ This CD-ROM includes the entire Student Edition test along with the English workbooks listed above.

TeacherWorks Plus™ All of the materials found in this booklet are included for viewing, printing, and editing in this CD-ROM.

Spanish Assessment Masters (ISBN10: 0-07-877350-4, ISBN13: 978-0-07-877350-1) These masters contain a Spanish version of Chapter 5 Test Form 2A and Form 2C.

 Glencoe

The McGraw·Hill Companies

Send all inquiries to:
Glencoe/McGraw-Hill
8787 Orion Place
Columbus, OH 43240

ISBN13: 978-0-07-873962-0
ISBN10: 0-07-873962-4

Geometry CRM5

Printed in the United States of America

1 2 3 4 5 6 7 8 9 10 009 13 12 11 10 09 08 07 06

CONTENTS

Teacher's Guide to Using the
Chapter 5 Resource Masters

The *Chapter 5 Resource Masters* includes the core materials needed for Chapter 5. These materials include worksheets, extensions, and assessment options. The answers for these pages appear at the back of this booklet.

All of the materials found in this booklet are included for viewing and printing on the *TeacherWorks Plus*™ CD-ROM.

Chapter Resources

Student-Built Glossary (pages 1–2) These masters are a student study tool that presents up to twenty of the key vocabulary terms from the chapter. Students are to record definitions and/or examples for each term. You may suggest that students highlight or star the terms with which they are not familiar. Give this to students before beginning Lesson 5-1. Encourage them to add these pages to their mathematics study notebooks. Remind them to complete the appropriate words as they study each lesson.

Anticipation Guide (pages 3–4) This master, presented in both English and Spanish, is a survey used before beginning the chapter to pinpoint what students may or may not know about the concepts in the chapter. Students will revisit this survey after they complete the chapter to see if their perceptions have changed.

Lesson Resources

Lesson Reading Guide Get Ready for the Lesson extends the discussion from the beginning of the Student Edition lesson. Read the Lesson asks students to interpret the context of and relationships among terms in the lesson. Finally, Remember What You Learned asks students to summarize what they have learned using various representation techniques. Use as a study tool for note taking or as an informal reading assignment. It is also a helpful tool for ELL (English Language Learners).

Study Guide and Intervention These masters provide vocabulary, key concepts, additional worked-out examples and Check Your Progress exercises to use as a reteaching activity. It can also be used in conjunction with the Student Edition as an instructional tool for students who have been absent.

Skills Practice This master focuses more on the computational nature of the lesson. Use as an additional practice option or as homework for second-day teaching of the lesson.

Practice This master closely follows the types of problems found in the Exercises section of the Student Edition and includes word problems. Use as an additional practice option or as homework for second-day teaching of the lesson.

Word Problem Practice This master includes additional practice in solving word problems that apply the concepts of the lesson. Use as an additional practice or as homework for second-day teaching of the lesson.

Enrichment These activities may extend the concepts of the lesson, offer a historical or multicultural look at the concepts, or widen students' perspectives on the mathematics they are learning. They are written for use with all levels of students.

Graphing Calculator, Scientific Calculator, or Spreadsheet Activities
These activities present ways in which technology can be used with the concepts in some lessons of this chapter. Use as an alternative approach to some concepts or as an integral part of your lesson presentation.

Assessment Options
The assessment masters in the *Chapter 5 Resource Masters* offer a wide range of assessment tools for formative (monitoring) assessment and summative (final) assessment.

Student Recording Sheet This master corresponds with the standardized test practice at the end of the chapter.

Pre-AP Rubric This master provides information for teachers and students on how to assess performance on open-ended questions.

Quizzes Four free-response quizzes offer assessment at appropriate intervals in the chapter.

Mid-Chapter Test This 1-page test provides an option to assess the first half of the chapter. It parallels the timing of the Mid-Chapter Quiz in the Student Edition and includes both multiple-choice and free-response questions.

Vocabulary Test This test is suitable for all students. It includes a list of vocabulary words and 10 questions to assess students' knowledge of those words. This can also be used in conjunction with one of the leveled chapter tests.

Leveled Chapter Tests
- *Form 1* contains multiple-choice questions and is intended for use with below grade level students.
- *Forms 2A and 2B* contain multiple-choice questions aimed at on grade level students. These tests are similar in format to offer comparable testing situations.
- *Forms 2C and 2D* contain free-response questions aimed at on grade level students. These tests are similar in format to offer comparable testing situations.
- *Form 3* is a free-response test for use with above grade level students.

All of the above mentioned tests include a free-response Bonus question.

Extended-Response Test Performance assessment tasks are suitable for all students. Sample answers and a scoring rubric are included for evaluation.

Standardized Test Practice These three pages are cumulative in nature. It includes three parts: multiple-choice questions with bubble-in answer format, griddable questions with answer grids, and short-answer free-response questions.

Answers
- The answers for the Anticipation Guide and Lesson Resources are provided as reduced pages with answers appearing in red.
- Full-size answer keys are provided for the assessment masters.

5 Student-Built Glossary

This is an alphabetical list of the key vocabulary terms you will learn in Chapter 5. As you study the chapter, complete each term's definition or description. Remember to add the page number where you found the term. Add these pages to your Geometry Study Notebook to review vocabulary at the end of the chapter.

Vocabulary Term	Found on Page	Definition/Description/Example
altitude		
centroid		
circumcenter SUHR·kuhm·SEN·tuhr		
concurrent lines		
incenter		
indirect proof		

(continued on the next page)

5 Student-Built Glossary *(continued)*

Vocabulary Term	Found on Page	Definition/Description/Example
indirect reasoning		
median		
orthocenter OHR·thoh·CEN·tuhr		
perpendicular bisector		
point of concurrency		
proof by contradiction		

5 Anticipation Guide

Relationships in Triangles

STEP 1 *Before you begin Chapter 5*

- Read each statement.
- Decide whether you Agree (A) or Disagree (D) with the statement.
- Write A or D in the first column OR if you are not sure whether you agree or disagree, write NS (Not Sure).

STEP 1 A, D, or NS	Statement	STEP 2 A or D
	1. Any point that is on the perpendicular bisector of a segment is equidistant from the endpoints of that segment.	
	2. The circumcenter of a triangle is equidistant from the midpoints of each side of the triangle.	
	3. Three or more parallel lines are called concurrent lines.	
	4. Three altitudes can be drawn for any one triangle.	
	5. A median of a triangle is any segment that contains the midpoint of a side of the triangle.	
	6. The measure of an exterior angle of a triangle is always greater than the measures of either of its corresponding remote interior angles.	
	7. The longest side in a triangle is opposite the smallest angle in that triangle.	
	8. To write an indirect proof that two lines are perpendicular, begin by assuming the two lines are not perpendicular.	
	9. The length of the longest side of a triangle is always greater than the sum of the lengths of the other two sides.	
	10. In two triangles, if two pairs of sides are congruent, then the measure of the included angles determines which triangle has the longer third side.	

STEP 2 *After you complete Chapter 5*

- Reread each statement and complete the last column by entering an A or a D.
- Did any of your opinions about the statements change from the first column?
- For those statements that you mark with a D, use a piece of paper to write an example of why you disagree.

5 Ejercicios preparatorios

Relaciones en triángulos

PASO 1 *Antes de comenzar el Capítulo 5*

- Lee cada enunciado.
- Decide si estás de acuerdo (A) o en desacuerdo (D) con el enunciado.
- Escribe A o D en la primera columna O si no estás seguro(a) de la respuesta, escribe NS (No estoy seguro(a).

PASO 1 A, D o NS	Enunciado	PASO 2 A o D
	1. Cualquier punto ubicado sobre la mediatriz de un segmento, equidista de los extremos de dicho segmento.	
	2. El circuncentro del triángulo equidista de los puntos medios de cada lado del triángulo.	
	3. Tres o más rectas paralelas se llaman rectas concurrentes.	
	4. Se pueden dibujar tres alturas para cualquier triángulo.	
	5. La mediana de un triángulo es un segmento que contiene el punto medio de un lado del triángulo.	
	6. La medida del ángulo exterior de un triángulo es siempre mayor que las medidas de cualquiera de sus ángulos interiores no adyacentes.	
	7. El lado más largo en un triángulo está en el lado opuesto al ángulo más pequeño de éste.	
	8. Para escribir una prueba indirecta de que dos rectas son perpendiculares, comienza por suponer que las dos rectas no son perpendiculares.	
	9. La longitud del lado más largo de un triángulo es siempre mayor que la suma de los otros dos lados.	
	10. En dos triángulos, si dos pares de lados son congruentes, entonces la medida de los ángulos inscritos determina qué triángulo tiene el tercer lado más largo.	

PASO 2 *Después de completar el Capítulo 5*

- Vuelve a leer cada enunciado y completa la última columna con una A o una D.
- ¿Cambió cualquiera de tus opiniones sobre los enunciados de la primera columna?
- En una hoja de papel aparte, escribe un ejemplo de por qué estás en desacuerdo con los enunciados que marcaste con una D.

5-1 Lesson Reading Guide

Bisectors, Medians, and Altitudes

Lesson 5-1

Get Ready for the Lesson

Read the introduction to Lesson 5-1 in your textbook.

Draw any triangle and connect each vertex to the midpoint of the opposite side to form the three medians of the triangle. Is the point where the three medians intersect the midpoint of each of the medians?

Read the Lesson

1. Underline the correct word or phrase to complete each sentence.

   a. Three or more lines that intersect at a common point are called (parallel/perpendicular/concurrent) lines.

   b. Any point on the perpendicular bisector of a segment is (parallel to/congruent to/equidistant from) the endpoints of the segment.

   c. A(n) (altitude/angle bisector/median/perpendicular bisector) of a triangle is a segment drawn from a vertex of the triangle perpendicular to the line containing the opposite side.

   d. The point of concurrency of the three perpendicular bisectors of a triangle is called the (orthocenter/circumcenter/centroid/incenter).

   e. Any point in the interior of an angle that is equidistant from the sides of that angle lies on the (median/angle bisector/altitude).

   f. The point of concurrency of the three angle bisectors of a triangle is called the (orthocenter/circumcenter/centroid/incenter).

2. In the figure, E is the midpoint of $\overline{AB}$, F is the midpoint of $\overline{BC}$, and G is the midpoint of $\overline{AC}$.

   a. Name the altitudes of $\triangle ABC$.

   b. Name the medians of $\triangle ABC$.

   c. Name the centroid of $\triangle ABC$.

   d. Name the orthocenter of $\triangle ABC$.

   e. If $AF = 12$ and $CE = 9$, find AH and HE.

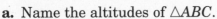

Remember What You Learned

3. A good way to remember something is to explain it to someone else. Suppose that a classmate is having trouble remembering whether the center of gravity of a triangle is the orthocenter, the centroid, the incenter, or the circumcenter of the triangle. Suggest a way to remember which point it is.

5-1 Study Guide and Intervention

Bisectors, Medians, and Altitudes

Perpendicular Bisectors and Angle Bisectors A **perpendicular bisector** of a side of a triangle is a line, segment, or ray in the same plane as the triangle that is perpendicular to the side and passes through its midpoint. Another special segment, ray, or line is an **angle bisector**, which divides an angle into two congruent angles.

Two properties of perpendicular bisectors are:

(1) a point is on the perpendicular bisector of a segment if and only if it is equidistant from the endpoints of the segment, and

(2) the three perpendicular bisectors of the sides of a triangle meet at a point, called the **circumcenter** of the triangle, that is equidistant from the three vertices of the triangle.

Two properties of angle bisectors are:

(1) a point is on the angle bisector of an angle if and only if it is equidistant from the sides of the angle, and

(2) the three angle bisectors of a triangle meet at a point, called the **incenter** of the triangle, that is equidistant from the three sides of the triangle.

Example 1 $\overrightarrow{BD}$ is the perpendicular bisector of $\overline{AC}$. Find x.

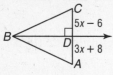

$\overrightarrow{BD}$ is the perpendicular bisector of $\overline{AC}$, so $AD = DC$.

$$3x + 8 = 5x - 6$$
$$14 = 2x$$
$$7 = x$$

Example 2 $\overrightarrow{MR}$ is the angle bisector of $\angle NMP$. Find x if $m\angle 1 = 5x + 8$ and $m\angle 2 = 8x - 16$.

$\overrightarrow{MR}$ is the angle bisector of $\angle NMP$, so $m\angle 1 = m\angle 2$.

$$5x + 8 = 8x - 16$$
$$24 = 3x$$
$$8 = x$$

Exercises

Find the value of each variable.

1.

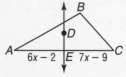

$\overrightarrow{DE}$ is the perpendicular bisector of $\overline{AC}$.

2.

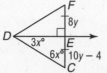

$\triangle CDF$ is equilateral.

3.

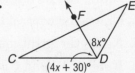

$\overrightarrow{DF}$ bisects $\angle CDE$.

4. For what kinds of triangle(s) can the perpendicular bisector of a side also be an angle bisector of the angle opposite the side?

5. For what kind of triangle do the perpendicular bisectors intersect in a point outside the triangle?

5-1 Study Guide and Intervention (continued)

Bisectors, Medians, and Altitudes

Medians and Altitudes A **median** is a line segment that connects the vertex of a triangle to the midpoint of the opposite side. The three medians of a triangle intersect at the **centroid** of the triangle.

Centroid Theorem	The centroid of a triangle is located two thirds of the distance from a vertex to the midpoint of the side opposite the vertex on a median.

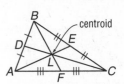

$$AL = \frac{2}{3}AE, \ BL = \frac{2}{3}BF, \ CL = \frac{2}{3}CD$$

Example Points R, S, and T are the midpoints of $\overline{AB}$, $\overline{BC}$ and $\overline{AC}$, respectively. Find x, y, and z.

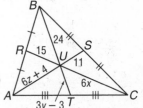

$$CU = \frac{2}{3}CR \qquad BU = \frac{2}{3}BT \qquad AU = \frac{2}{3}AS$$
$$6x = \frac{2}{3}(6x + 15) \quad 24 = \frac{2}{3}(24 + 3y - 3) \quad 6z + 4 = \frac{2}{3}(6z + 4 + 11)$$
$$9x = 6x + 15 \qquad 36 = 24 + 3y - 3 \qquad \frac{3}{2}(6z + 4) = 6z + 4 + 11$$
$$3x = 15 \qquad 36 = 21 + 3y \qquad 9z + 6 = 6z + 15$$
$$x = 5 \qquad 15 = 3y \qquad 3z = 9$$
$$\qquad 5 = y \qquad z = 3$$

Exercises

Find the value of each variable.

1.

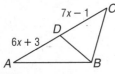

$7x - 1$
$6x + 3$

$\overline{BD}$ is a median.

2.

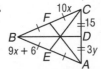

$10x$
15
$9x + 6$
$3y$

$AB = CB$; D, E, and F are midpoints.

3.

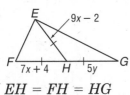

$9x - 2$
$7x + 4 \quad 5y$

$EH = FH = HG$

4. M, O, P are midpoints.

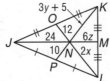

$3y + 5$
$24 \quad 12 \quad 6z$
$10 \quad 2x$

5.

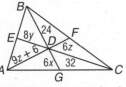

$8y \quad 24$
$9z + 6 \quad 6z$
$6x \quad 32$

D is the centroid of $\triangle ABC$.

6.

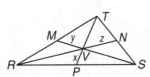

$y \quad z$
$x \quad V$

V is the centroid of $\triangle RST$;
$TP = 18$; $MS = 15$; $RN = 24$

7. For what kind of triangle are the medians and angle bisectors the same segments?

8. For what kind of triangle is the centroid outside the triangle?

Lesson 5-1

5-1 **Skills Practice**

Bisectors, Medians, and Altitudes

ALGEBRA For Exercises 1–4, use the given information to find each value.

1. Find x if $\overline{EG}$ is a median of $\triangle DEF$.

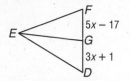

2. Find x and RT if $\overline{SU}$ is a median of $\triangle RST$.

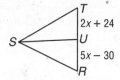

3. Find x and EF if $\overline{BD}$ is an angle bisector.

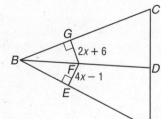

4. Find x and IJ if $\overline{HK}$ is an altitude of $\triangle HIJ$.

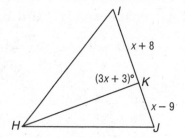

ALGEBRA For Exercises 5–7, use the following information.

In $\triangle LMN$, P, Q, and R are the midpoints of $\overline{LM}$, $\overline{MN}$, and $\overline{LN}$, respectively.

5. Find x.

6. Find y.

7. Find z.

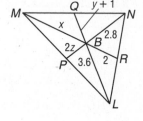

ALGEBRA Lines a, b, and c are perpendicular bisectors of $\triangle PQR$ and meet at A.

8. Find x.

9. Find y.

10. Find z.

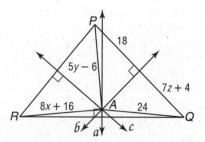

COORDINATE GEOMETRY The vertices of $\triangle HIJ$ are $J(1, 0)$, $H(6, 0)$, and $I(3, 6)$. Find the coordinates of the points of concurrency of $\triangle HIJ$.

11. orthocenter

12. centroid

13. circumcenter

5-1 Practice

Bisectors, Medians, and Altitudes

ALGEBRA In $\triangle ABC$, $\overline{BF}$ is the angle bisector of $\angle ABC$, $\overline{AE}$, $\overline{BF}$, and $\overline{CD}$ are medians, and P is the centroid.

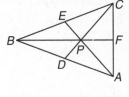

1. Find x if $DP = 4x - 3$ and $CP = 30$.

2. Find y if $AP = y$ and $EP = 18$.

3. Find z if $FP = 5z + 10$ and $BP = 42$.

4. If $m\angle ABC = x$ and $m\angle BAC = m\angle BCA = 2x - 10$, is $\overline{BF}$ an altitude? Explain.

ALGEBRA In $\triangle PRS$, $\overline{PT}$ is an altitude and $\overline{PX}$ is a median.

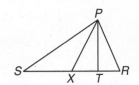

5. Find RS if $RX = x + 7$ and $SX = 3x - 11$.

6. Find RT if $RT = x - 6$ and $m\angle PTR = 8x - 6$.

ALGEBRA In $\triangle DEF$, $\overline{GI}$ is a perpendicular bisector.

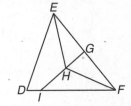

7. Find x if $EH = 16$ and $FH = 6x - 5$.

8. Find y if $EG = 3.2y - 1$ and $FG = 2y + 5$.

9. Find z if $m\angle EGH = 12z$.

COORDINATE GEOMETRY The vertices of $\triangle STU$ are $S(0, 1)$, $T(4, 7)$, and $U(8, -3)$. Find the coordinates of the points of concurrency of $\triangle STU$.

10. orthocenter   11. centroid   12. circumcenter

13. **MOBILES** Nabuko wants to construct a mobile out of flat triangles so that the surfaces of the triangles hang parallel to the floor when the mobile is suspended. How can Nabuko be certain that she hangs the triangles to achieve this effect?

Lesson 5-1

5-1 Word Problem Practice

Bisectors, Medians, and Altitudes

1. **BALANCING** Johanna balanced a triangle flat on her finger tip. What point of the triangle must Johanna be touching?

2. **PICNICS** Marsha and Bill are going to the park for a picnic. The park is triangular. One side of the park is bordered by a river and the other two sides are bordered by busy streets. Marsha and Bill want to find a spot that is equally far away from the river and the streets. At what point in the park should they set up their picnic?

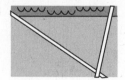

3. **MOVING** Martin has 3 grown children. The figure shows the locations of Martin's children on a map that has a coordinate plane on it. Martin would like to move to a location that is the same distance from all three of his children. What are the coordinates of the location on the map that is equidistant from all three children?

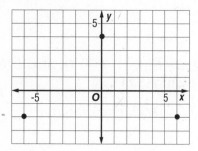

4. **NEIGHBORHOOD** Amanda is looking at her neighborhood map. She notices that her house along with the homes of her friends Brian, and Cathy can be the vertices of a triangle. The map is on a coordinate grid. Amanda's house is at the point (1, 3) Brian's is at (5, −1), and Cathy's is at (4, 5). Where would the three friends meet if they each left their houses at the same time and walked to the opposite side of the triangle along the path of shortest distance from their house?

PLAZAS For Exercises 5–7, use the following information.

An architect is designing a triangular plaza. For aesthetic purposes, the architect pays special attention to the location of the centroid C and the circumcenter O.

5. Give an example of a triangular plaza where $C = O$. If no such example exists, state that this is *impossible*.

6. Give an example of a triangular plaza where C is inside the plaza and O is outside the plaza. If no such example exists, state that this is *impossible*.

7. Give an example of a triangular plaza where C is outside the plaza and O is inside the plaza. If no such example exists, state that this is *impossible*.

5-1 Enrichment

Lesson 5-1

Inscribed and Circumscribed Circles

The three angle bisectors of a triangle intersect in a single point called the **incenter**. This point is the center of a circle that just touches the three sides of the triangle. Except for the three points where the circle touches the sides, the circle is inside the triangle. The circle is said to be inscribed in the triangle.

1. With a compass and a straightedge, construct the inscribed circle for $\triangle PQR$ by following the steps below.

   Step 1 Construct the bisectors of $\angle R$ and $\angle Q$. Label the point where the bisectors meet A.

   Step 2 Construct a perpendicular segment from A to $\overline{RQ}$. Use the letter B to label the point where the perpendicular segment intersects $\overline{RQ}$.

   Step 3 Use a compass to draw the circle with center at A and radius $\overline{AB}$.

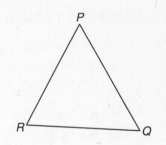

Construct the inscribed circle in each triangle.

2.

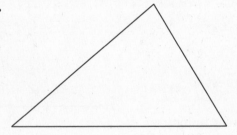

3.

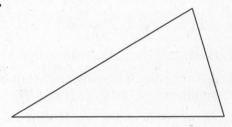

The three perpendicular bisectors of the sides of a triangle also meet in a single point. This point is the center of the circumscribed circle, which passes through each vertex of the triangle. Except for the three points where the circle touches the triangle, the circle is outside the triangle.

4. Follow the steps below to construct the circumscribed circle for $\triangle FGH$.

   Step 1 Construct the perpendicular bisectors of $\overline{FG}$ and $\overline{FH}$. Use the letter A to label the point where the perpendicular bisectors meet.

   Step 2 Draw the circle that has center A and radius $\overline{AF}$.

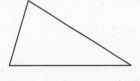

Construct the circumscribed circle for each triangle.

5.

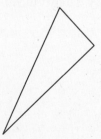

6.

5-2 Lesson Reading Guide

Inequalities and Triangles

Get Ready for the Lesson

Read the introduction to Lesson 5-2 in your textbook.

- Which side of the patio is opposite the largest corner?

- Which side of the patio is opposite the smallest corner?

Read the Lesson

1. Name the property of inequality that is illustrated by each of the following.

    a. If $x > 8$ and $8 > y$, then $x > y$.

    b. If $x < y$, then $x - 7.5 < y - 7.5$.

    c. If $x > y$, then $-3x < -3y$.

    d. If x is any real number, $x > 0$, $x = 0$, or $x < 0$.

2. Use the definition of inequality to write an *equation* that shows that each inequality is true.

    a. $20 > 12$ **b.** $101 > 99$

    c. $8 > -2$ **d.** $7 > -7$

    e. $-11 > -12$ **f.** $-30 > -45$

3. In the figure, $m\angle IJK = 45$ and $m\angle H > m\angle I$.

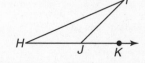

    a. Arrange the following angles in order from largest to smallest: $\angle I$, $\angle IJK$, $\angle H$, $\angle IJH$

    b. Arrange the sides of $\triangle HIJ$ in order from shortest to longest.

    c. Is $\triangle HIJ$ an acute, right, or obtuse triangle? Explain your reasoning.

    d. Is $\triangle HIJ$ scalene, isosceles, or equilateral? Explain your reasoning.

Remember What You Learned

4. A good way to remember a new geometric theorem is to relate it to a theorem you learned earlier. Explain how the Exterior Angle Inequality Theorem is related to the Exterior Angle Theorem, and why the Exterior Angle Inequality Theorem must be true if the Exterior Angle Theorem is true.

5-2 Study Guide and Intervention

Inequalities and Triangles

Angle Inequalities Properties of inequalities, including the Transitive, Addition, Subtraction, Multiplication, and Division Properties of Inequality, can be used with measures of angles and segments. There is also a Comparison Property of Inequality.

For any real numbers a and b, either $a < b$, $a = b$, or $a > b$.

The Exterior Angle Theorem can be used to prove this inequality involving an exterior angle.

Exterior Angle Inequality Theorem	If an angle is an exterior angle of a triangle, then its measure is greater than the measure of either of its corresponding remote interior angles.	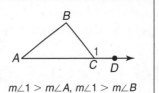 $m\angle 1 > m\angle A, m\angle 1 > m\angle B$

Example List all angles of $\triangle EFG$ whose measures are less than $m\angle 1$.

The measure of an exterior angle is greater than the measure of either remote interior angle. So $m\angle 3 < m\angle 1$ and $m\angle 4 < m\angle 1$.

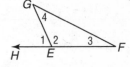

Exercises

List all angles that satisfy the stated condition.

1. all angles whose measures are less than $m\angle 1$

2. all angles whose measures are greater than $m\angle 3$

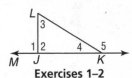
Exercises 1–2

3. all angles whose measures are less than $m\angle 1$

4. all angles whose measures are greater than $m\angle 1$

5. all angles whose measures are less than $m\angle 7$

6. all angles whose measures are greater than $m\angle 2$

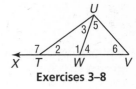
Exercises 3–8

7. all angles whose measures are greater than $m\angle 5$

8. all angles whose measures are less than $m\angle 4$

9. all angles whose measures are less than $m\angle 1$

10. all angles whose measures are greater than $m\angle 4$

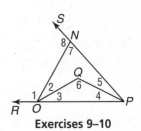
Exercises 9–10

Lesson 5-2

5-2 **Study Guide and Intervention** *(continued)*

Inequalities and Triangles

Angle-Side Relationships When the sides of triangles are not congruent, there is a relationship between the sides and angles of the triangles.

- If one side of a triangle is longer than another side, then the angle opposite the longer side has a greater measure than the angle opposite the shorter side.

- If one angle of a triangle has a greater measure than another angle, then the side opposite the greater angle is longer than the side opposite the lesser angle.

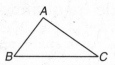

If $AC > AB$, then $m\angle B > m\angle C$.
If $m\angle A > m\angle C$, then $BC > AB$.

Example 1 List the angles in order from least to greatest measure.

$\angle T, \angle R, \angle S$

Example 2 List the sides in order from shortest to longest.

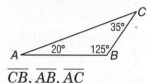

$\overline{CB}, \overline{AB}, \overline{AC}$

Exercises

List the angles or sides in order from least to greatest measure.

1.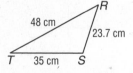

2.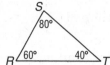

3.

Determine the relationship between the measures of the given angles.

4. $\angle R, \angle RUS$

5. $\angle T, \angle UST$

6. $\angle UVS, \angle R$

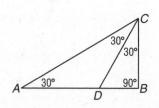

Determine the relationship between the lengths of the given sides.

7. $\overline{AC}, \overline{BC}$

8. $\overline{BC}, \overline{DB}$

9. $\overline{AC}, \overline{DB}$

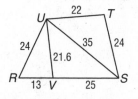

5-2 Skills Practice

Inequalities and Triangles

Determine which angle has the greatest measure.

1. $\angle 1, \angle 3, \angle 4$

2. $\angle 4, \angle 5, \angle 7$

3. $\angle 2, \angle 3, \angle 6$

4. $\angle 5, \angle 6, \angle 8$

Use the Exterior Angle Inequality Theorem to list all angles that satisfy the stated condition.

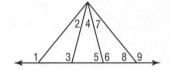

5. all angles whose measures are less than $m\angle 1$

6. all angles whose measures are less than $m\angle 9$

7. all angles whose measures are greater than $m\angle 5$

8. all angles whose measures are greater than $m\angle 8$

Determine the relationship between the measures of the given angles.

9. $m\angle ABD, m\angle BAD$

10. $m\angle ADB, m\angle BAD$

11. $m\angle BCD, m\angle CDB$

12. $m\angle CBD, m\angle CDB$

Determine the relationship between the lengths of the given sides.

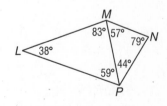

13. $\overline{LM}, \overline{LP}$

14. $\overline{MP}, \overline{MN}$

15. $\overline{MN}, \overline{NP}$

16. $\overline{MP}, \overline{LP}$

Lesson 5-2

5-2 Practice

Inequalities and Triangles

Determine which angle has the greatest measure.

1. ∠1, ∠3, ∠4

2. ∠4, ∠8, ∠9

3. ∠2, ∠3, ∠7

4. ∠7, ∠8, ∠10

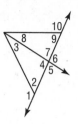

Use the Exterior Angle Inequality Theorem to list all angles that satisfy the stated condition.

5. all angles whose measures are less than $m\angle 1$

6. all angles whose measures are less than $m\angle 3$

7. all angles whose measures are greater than $m\angle 7$

8. all angles whose measures are greater than $m\angle 2$

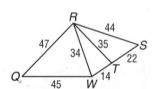

Determine the relationship between the measures of the given angles.

9. $m\angle QRW, m\angle RWQ$

10. $m\angle RTW, m\angle TWR$

11. $m\angle RST, m\angle TRS$

12. $m\angle WQR, m\angle QRW$

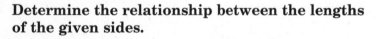

Determine the relationship between the lengths of the given sides.

13. $\overline{DH}, \overline{GH}$

14. $\overline{DE}, \overline{DG}$

15. $\overline{EG}, \overline{FG}$

16. $\overline{DE}, \overline{EG}$

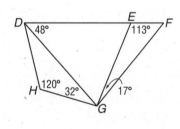

17. **SPORTS** The figure shows the position of three trees on one part of a Frisbee™ course. At which tree position is the angle between the trees the greatest?

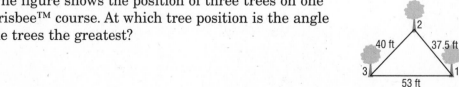

5-2 Word Problem Practice

Inequalities and Triangles

1. DISTANCE Carl and Rose live on the same straight road. From their balconies they can see a flagpole in the distance. The angle that each person's line of sight to the flagpole makes with the road is the same. How do their distances from the flagpole compare?

2. OBTUSE TRIANGLES Don notices that the side opposite the right angle in a right triangle is always the longest of the three sides. Is this also true of the side opposite the obtuse angle in an obtuse triangle? Explain.

3. STRING Jake built a triangular structure with three black sticks. He tied one end of a string to vertex M and the other end to a point on the stick opposite M, pulling the string taut. Prove that the length of the string cannot exceed the longer of the two sides of the structure.

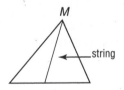

4. SQUARES Matthew has three different squares. He arranges the squares to form a triangle as shown. Based on the information, list the squares in order from the one with the smallest perimeter to the one with the largest perimeter.

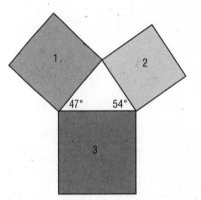

CITIES For Exercises 5 and 6, use the following information.

Stella is going to Texas to visit a friend. As she was looking at a map to see where she might want to go, she noticed the cities Austin, Dallas, and Abilene formed a triangle. She wanted to determine how the distances between the cities were related, so she used a protractor to measure two angles.

5. Based on the information in the figure, which of the two cities are nearest to each other?

6. Based on the information in the figure, which of the two cities are farthest apart from each other?

5-2 Enrichment

Construction Problem

The diagram below shows segment *AB* adjacent to a closed region. The problem requires that you construct another segment *XY* to the right of the closed region such that points *A*, *B*, *X*, and *Y* are collinear. You are not allowed to touch or cross the closed region with your compass or straightedge.

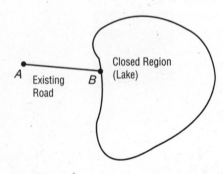

Follow these instructions to construct a segment XY so that it is collinear with segment AB.

1. Construct the perpendicular bisector of $\overline{AB}$. Label the midpoint as point *C*, and the line as *m*.

2. Mark two points *P* and *Q* on line *m* that lie well above the closed region. Construct the perpendicular bisector *n* of $\overline{PQ}$. Label the intersection of lines *m* and *n* as point *D*.

3. Mark points *R* and *S* on line *n* that lie well to the right of the closed region. Construct the perpendicular bisector *k* of $\overline{RS}$. Label the intersection of lines *n* and *k* as point *E*.

4. Mark point *X* on line *k* so that *X* is below line *n* and so that $\overline{EX}$ is congruent to $\overline{DC}$.

5. Mark points *T* and *V* on line *k* and on opposite sides of *X*, so that $\overline{XT}$ and $\overline{XV}$ are congruent. Construct the perpendicular bisector *ℓ* of $\overline{TV}$. Call the point where the line *ℓ* hits the boundary of the closed region point *Y*. $\overline{XY}$ corresponds to the new road.

5-2 Graphing Calculator Activity

Cabri Junior: Inequalities and Triangles

Cabri Junior can be used to investigate the relationships between angles and sides of a triangle.

Step 1 Use Cabri Jr. to draw and label a triangle.
- Select **F2 Triangle** to draw a triangle.
- Move the cursor to where you want the first vertex. Press ENTER .
- Repeat this procedure to determine the next two vertices of the triangle.
- Select **F5 Alph-num** to label each vertex.
- Move the cursor to a vertex, press ENTER , enter *A,* and press ENTER again.
- Repeat this procedure to label vertex *B* and vertex *C.*

Step 2 Draw an exterior angle of △*ABC.*
- Select **F2 Line** to draw a line through $\overline{BC}$.
- Select **F2 Point, Point on** to draw a point on $\overleftrightarrow{BC}$ so that *C* is between *B* and the new point.
- Select **F5 Alph-num** to label the point *D.*

Step 3 Find the measures of the three interior angles and the exterior angle, ∠*ACD.*
- Select **F5 Measure, Angle.**
- To find the measure of ∠*ABC,* select points *A, B,* and *C* (with the vertex *B* as the second point selected).
- Repeat to find the remaining angle measures.

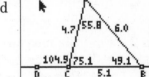

Step 4 Find the measure of each side of △*ABC.*
- Select **F5 Measure, D. & Length.**
- To find the length of $\overline{AB}$, select point *A* and then select point *B.*
- Repeat this procedure to find the lengths of $\overline{BC}$ and $\overline{CA}$.

Exercises

Analyze your drawing.

1. What is the relationship between *m*∠*ACD* and *m*∠*ABC*? *m*∠*ACD* and *m*∠*BAC*?

2. Make a conjecture about the relationship between the measures of an exterior angle (∠*ACD*) and its two remote interior angles (∠*ABC* and ∠*BAC*).

3. Change the dimensions of the triangle by moving point *A.* (Press CLEAR so the pointer becomes a black arrow. Move the pointer close to point *A* until the arrow becomes transparent and point *A* is blinking. Press ALPHA to change the arrow to a hand. Then move the point.) Is your conjecture still true?

4. Which side of the triangle is the longest? the shortest?

5. Which angle measure (not including the exterior angle) is the greatest? the least?

6. Make a conjecture about where the longest side is in relationship to the greatest angle and where the shortest side is in relationship to the least angle.

Lesson 5-2

5-2 Geometer's Sketchpad Activity

Inequalities and Triangles

The Geometer's Sketchpad can be used to investigate the relationships between angles and sides of a triangle.

Step 1 Use The Geometer's Sketchpad to draw a triangle and one exterior angle.
- Construct a ray by selecting the Ray tool from the toolbar. First, click where you want the first point. Then click a second point to draw the ray.
- Next, select the Segment tool from the toolbar. Use the endpoint of the ray as the first point for the segment and click on a second point to construct the segment.
- Construct another segment joining the second point of the previous segment to a point on the ray.

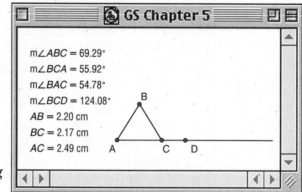

- Display the labels for each point. Use the Selection Arrow tool to select all four points. Display the labels by selecting **Show Label** from the **Display** menu.

Step 2 Find the measures of each angle.
- To find the measure of angle *ABC*, use the Selection Arrow tool to select points *A*, *B*, and *C* (with the vertex *B* as the second point selected). Then, under the **Measure** menu, select **Angle**. Use this method to find the remaining angle measures, including the exterior angle, ∠*BCD*.

Step 3 Find the measures of each side of the triangle.
- To find the measure of side *AB*, select *A* and then *B*. Next, under the **Measure** menu, select **Distance**. Use this method to find the other two sides.

Exercises

Analyze your drawing.

1. What is the relationship between *m*∠*BCD* and *m*∠*ABC*? *m*∠*BCD* and *m*∠*BAC*?

2. Make a conjecture about the relationship between the measures of an exterior angle (∠*BCD*) and its two remote interior angles (∠*ABC* and ∠*BAC*).

3. Change the dimensions of the triangle by selecting point *A* with the pointer tool and moving it. Is your conjecture still true?

4. Which side of the triangle is the longest? the shortest?

5. Which angle measure (not including the exterior angle) is the greatest? the least?

6. Make a conjecture about where the longest side is in relationship to the greatest angle and where the shortest side is in relationship to the least angle.

5-3 Lesson Reading Guide

Indirect Proof

Get Ready for the Lesson

Read the introduction to Lesson 5-3 in your textbook.

How could the author of a murder mystery use indirect reasoning to show that a particular suspect is not guilty?

_____

_____

Read the Lesson

1. Supply the missing words to complete the list of steps involved in writing an indirect proof.

   Step 1 Assume that the conclusion is _____.

   Step 2 Show that this assumption leads to a _____ of the

   _____ or some other fact, such as a definition, postulate,

   _____, or corollary.

   Step 3 Point out that the assumption must be _____ and, therefore, the

   conclusion must be _____.

2. State the assumption that you would make to start an indirect proof of each statement.

   a. If $-6x > 30$, then $x < -5$.

   b. If n is a multiple of 6, then n is a multiple of 3.

   c. If a and b are both odd, then ab is odd.

   d. If a is positive and b is negative, then ab is negative.

   e. If F is between E and D, then $EF + FD = ED$.

   f. In a plane, if two lines are perpendicular to the same line, then they are parallel.

   g. Refer to the figure.

   If $AB = AC$, then $m\angle B = m\angle C$.

   h. Refer to the figure.

   In $\triangle PQR$, $PR + QR > QP$.

Remember What You Learned

3. A good way to remember a new concept in mathematics is to relate it to something you have already learned. How is the process of indirect proof related to the relationship between a conditional statement and its contrapositive?

Lesson 5-3

5-3 Study Guide and Intervention

Indirect Proof

Indirect Proof with Algebra One way to prove that a statement is true is to assume that its conclusion is false and then show that this assumption leads to a contradiction of the hypothesis, a definition, postulate, theorem, or other statement that is accepted as true. That contradiction means that the conclusion cannot be false, so the conclusion must be true. This is known as **indirect proof**.

Steps for Writing an Indirect Proof

1. Assume that the conclusion is false.
2. Show that this assumption leads to a contradiction.
3. Point out that the assumption must be false, and therefore, the conclusion must be true.

Example   Given: $3x + 5 > 8$
Prove: $x > 1$

Step 1 Assume that x is not greater than 1. That is, $x = 1$ or $x < 1$.

Step 2 Make a table for several possibilities for $x = 1$ or $x < 1$. The contradiction is that when $x = 1$ or $x < 1$, then $3x + 5$ is not greater than 8.

Step 3 This contradicts the given information that $3x + 5 > 8$. The assumption that x is not greater than 1 must be false, which means that the statement "$x > 1$" must be true.

x	$3x + 5$
1	8
0	5
−1	2
−2	−1
−3	−4

Exercises

Write the assumption you would make to start an indirect proof of each statement.

1. If $2x > 14$, then $x > 7$.

2. For all real numbers, if $a + b > c$, then $a > c - b$.

Complete the proof.

Given: n is an integer and n^2 is even.

Prove: n is even.

3. Assume that _____

4. Then n can be expressed as $2a + 1$ by _____

5. $n^2 =$ _____   Substitution

6. $=$ _____   Multiply.

7. $=$ _____   Simplify.

8. $= 2(2a^2 + 2a) + 1$ _____

9. $2(2a^2 + 2a) + 1$ is an odd number. This contradicts the given that n^2 is even, so the assumption must be _____

10. Therefore, _____

5-3 Study Guide and Intervention (continued)

Indirect Proof

Indirect Proof with Geometry To write an indirect proof in geometry, you assume that the conclusion is false. Then you show that the assumption leads to a contradiction. The contradiction shows that the conclusion cannot be false, so it must be true.

Example Given: $m\angle C = 100$
Prove: $\angle A$ is not a right angle.

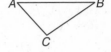

Step 1 Assume that $\angle A$ is a right angle.

Step 2 Show that this leads to a contradiction. If $\angle A$ is a right angle, then $m\angle A = 90$ and $m\angle C + m\angle A = 100 + 90 = 190$. Thus the sum of the measures of the angles of $\triangle ABC$ is greater than 180.

Step 3 The conclusion that the sum of the measures of the angles of $\triangle ABC$ is greater than 180 is a contradiction of a known property. The assumption that $\angle A$ is a right angle must be false, which means that the statement "$\angle A$ is not a right angle" must be true.

Exercises

Write the assumption you would make to start an indirect proof of each statement.

1. If $m\angle A = 90$, then $m\angle B = 45$.

2. If $\overline{AV}$ is not congruent to $\overline{VE}$, then $\triangle AVE$ is not isosceles.

Complete the proof.
Given: $\angle 1 \cong \angle 2$ and $\overline{DG}$ is not congruent to $\overline{FG}$.
Prove: $\overline{DE}$ is not congruent to $\overline{FE}$.

3. Assume that _____   Assume the conclusion is false.

4. $\overline{EG} \cong \overline{EG}$ _____

5. $\triangle EDG \cong \triangle EFG$ _____

6. _____

7. This contradicts the given information, so the assumption must

   be _____

8. Therefore, _____

Lesson 5-3

5-3 Skills Practice

Indirect Proof

Write the assumption you would make to start an indirect proof of each statement.

1. $m\angle ABC < m\angle CBA$

2. $\triangle DEF \cong \triangle RST$

3. Line a is perpendicular to line b.

4. $\angle 5$ is supplementary to $\angle 6$.

PROOF Write an indirect proof.

5. **Given:** $x^2 + 8 \le 12$
   Prove: $x \le 2$

6. **Given:** $\angle D \not\cong \angle F$.
   Prove: $DE \ne EF$

5-3 Practice

Indirect Proof

Write the assumption you would make to start an indirect proof of each statement.

1. $\overline{BD}$ bisects $\angle ABC$.

2. $RT = TS$

PROOF Write an indirect proof.

3. **Given:** $-4x + 2 < -10$
   Prove: $x > 3$

4. **Given:** $m\angle 2 + m\angle 3 \neq 180$
   Prove: $a \nparallel b$

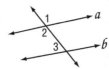

5. **PHYSICS** Sound travels through air at about 344 meters per second when the temperature is 20°C. If Enrique lives 2 kilometers from the fire station and it takes 5 seconds for the sound of the fire station siren to reach him, how can you prove indirectly that it is not 20°C when Enrique hears the siren?

Lesson 5-3

5-3 Word Problem Practice

Indirect Proof

1. CANOES Thirty-five students went on a canoeing expedition. They rented 17 canoes for the trip. Use an indirect proof to show that at least one canoe had more than two students in it.

2. AREA The area of the United States is about 6,000,000 square miles. The area of Hawaii is about 11,000 square miles. Use an indirect proof to show that at least one of the fifty states has an area greater than 120,000 square miles.

3. CONSECUTIVE NUMBERS David was trying to find a common factor other than 1 between various pairs of consecutive integers. Write an indirect proof to show David that two consecutive integers do not share a common factor other than 1.

4. WORDS The words *accomplishment*, *counterexample*, and *extemporaneous* all have 14 letters. Use an indirect proof to show that any word with 14 letters must use a repeated letter or have two letters that are consecutive in the alphabet.

LATTICE TRIANGLES For Exercises 5 and 6, use the following information.

A *lattice point* is a point whose coordinates are both integers. A lattice triangle is a triangle whose vertices are lattice points. It is a fact that a lattice triangle has an area of at least 0.5 square units.

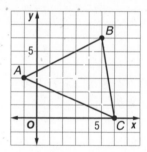

5. Suppose $\triangle ABC$ has a lattice point in its interior. Show that the lattice triangle can be partitioned into three smaller lattice triangles.

6. Prove indirectly that a lattice triangle with area 0.5 square units contains no lattice point. (Being on the boundary does not count as inside.)

5-3 Enrichment

More Counterexamples

Some statements in mathematics can be proven false by **counterexamples.** Consider the following statement.

For any numbers a and b, $a - b = b - a$.

You can prove that this statement is false in general if you can find one example for which the statement is false.

Let $a = 7$ and $b = 3$. Substitute these values in the equation above.

$$7 - 3 \stackrel{?}{=} 3 - 7$$
$$4 \neq -4$$

In general, for any numbers a and b, the statement $a - b = b - a$ is false. You can make the equivalent verbal statement: subtraction is *not* a commutative operation.

In each of the following exercises a, b, and c are any numbers. Prove that the statement is false by counterexample.

1. $a - (b - c) \stackrel{?}{=} (a - b) - c$

2. $a \div (b \div c) \stackrel{?}{=} (a \div b) \div c$

3. $a \div b \stackrel{?}{=} b \div a$

4. $a \div (b + c) \stackrel{?}{=} (a \div b) + (a \div c)$

5. $a + (bc) \stackrel{?}{=} (a + b)(a + c)$

6. $a^2 + a^2 \stackrel{?}{=} a^4$

7. Write the verbal equivalents for Exercises 1, 2, and 3.

8. For the Distributive Property $a(b + c) = ab + ac$ it is said that multiplication distributes over addition. Exercises 4 and 5 prove that some operations do not distribute. Write a statement for each exercise that indicates this.

Lesson 5-3

5-4 Lesson Reading Guide

The Triangle Inequality

Get Ready for the Lesson

Read the introduction to Lesson 5-4 in your textbook.

If you assume that non-stop flights go directly to their destination, why will it take longer to get to Albuquerque from any city if you take two flights rather than one?

Read the Lesson

1. Refer to the figure.

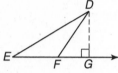

Which statements are true?

A. $DE > EF + FD$ **B.** $DE = EF + FD$

C. $EG = EF + FG$ **D.** $ED + DG > EG$

E. The shortest distance from D to $\overleftrightarrow{EG}$ is DF.

F. The shortest distance from D to $\overleftrightarrow{EG}$ is DG.

2. Complete each sentence about $\triangle XYZ$.

a. If $XY = 8$ and $YZ = 11$, then the range of values for XZ is _____ $< XZ <$ _____.

b. If $XY = 13$ and $XZ = 25$, then YZ must be between _____ and _____.

c. If $\triangle XYZ$ is isosceles with $\angle Z$ as the vertex angle, and $XZ = 8.5$, then the range of values for XY is _____ $< XY <$ _____.

d. If $XZ = a$ and $YZ = b$, with $b < a$, then the range for XY is _____ $< XY <$ _____.

Remember What You Learned

3. A good way to remember a new theorem is to state it informally in different words. How could you restate the Triangle Inequality Theorem?

5-4 Study Guide and Intervention

The Triangle Inequality

The Triangle Inequality If you take three straws of lengths 8 inches, 5 inches, and 1 inch and try to make a triangle with them, you will find that it is not possible. This illustrates the Triangle Inequality Theorem.

Triangle Inequality Theorem	The sum of the lengths of any two sides of a triangle is greater than the length of the third side.	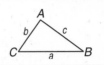

Example The measures of two sides of a triangle are 5 and 8. Find a range for the length of the third side.

By the Triangle Inequality, all three of the following inequalities must be true.

$5 + x > 8$ $8 + x > 5$ $5 + 8 > x$
$\quad x > 3$ $\quad\quad x > -3$ $\quad\quad 13 > x$

Therefore x must be between 3 and 13.

Exercises

Determine whether the given measures can be the lengths of the sides of a triangle. Write *yes* or *no*.

1. 3, 4, 6

2. 6, 9, 15

3. 8, 8, 8

4. 2, 4, 5

5. 4, 8, 16

6. 1.5, 2.5, 3

Find the range for the measure of the third side given the measures of two sides.

7. 1 and 6

8. 12 and 18

9. 1.5 and 5.5

10. 82 and 8

11. Suppose you have three different positive numbers arranged in order from least to greatest. What single comparison will let you see if the numbers can be the lengths of the sides of a triangle?

Lesson 5-4

5-4 Study Guide and Intervention (continued)

The Triangle Inequality

Distance Between a Point and a Line

The perpendicular segment from a point to a line is the shortest segment from the point to the line.

$\overline{PC}$ is the shortest segment from P to $\overleftrightarrow{AB}$.

The perpendicular segment from a point to a plane is the shortest segment from the point to the plane.

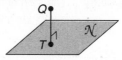

$\overline{QT}$ is the shortest segment from Q to plane $\mathcal{N}$.

Example Given: Point P is equidistant from the sides of an angle.

Prove: $\overline{BA} \cong \overline{CA}$

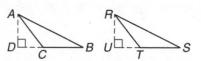

Proof:

1. Draw $\overline{BP}$ and $\overline{CP} \perp$ to the sides of $\angle RAS$.
2. $\angle PBA$ and $\angle PCA$ are right angles.
3. $\triangle ABP$ and $\triangle ACP$ are right triangles.
4. $\angle PBA \cong \angle PCA$
5. P is equidistant from the sides of $\angle RAS$.
6. $\overline{BP} \cong \overline{CP}$
7. $\overline{AP} \cong \overline{AP}$
8. $\triangle ABP \cong \triangle ACP$
9. $\overline{BA} \cong \overline{CA}$

1. Dist. is measured along a $\perp$.
2. Def. of $\perp$ lines
3. Def. of rt. $\triangle$
4. Rt. angles are $\cong$.
5. Given
6. Def. of equidistant
7. Reflexive Property
8. HL
9. CPCTC

Exercises

Complete the proof.

Given: $\triangle ABC \cong \triangle RST$; $\angle D \cong \angle U$

Prove: $\overline{AD} \cong \overline{RU}$

Proof:

1. $\triangle ABC \cong \triangle RST$; $\angle D \cong \angle U$

1. _____

2. $\overline{AC} \cong \overline{RT}$

2. _____

3. $\angle ACB \cong \angle RTS$

3. _____

4. $\angle ACB$ and $\angle ACD$ are a linear pair; $\angle RTS$ and $\angle RTU$ are a linear pair.

4. Def. of _____

5. $\angle ACB$ and $\angle ACD$ are supplementary; $\angle RTS$ and $\angle RTU$ are supplementary.

5. _____

6. _____

6. Angles suppl. to $\cong$ angles are $\cong$.

7. $\triangle ADC \cong \triangle RUT$

7. _____

8. _____

8. CPCTC

5-4 Skills Practice

The Triangle Inequality

Determine whether the given measures can be the lengths of the sides of a triangle. Write *yes* or *no*.

1. 2, 3, 4

2. 5, 7, 9

3. 4, 8, 11

4. 13, 13, 26

5. 9, 10, 20

6. 15, 17, 19

7. 14, 17, 31

8. 6, 7, 12

Find the range for the measure of the third side of a triangle given the measures of two sides.

9. 5 and 9

10. 7 and 14

11. 8 and 13

12. 10 and 12

13. 12 and 15

14. 15 and 27

15. 17 and 28

16. 18 and 22

ALGEBRA Determine whether the given coordinates are the vertices of a triangle. Explain.

17. $A(3, 5)$, $B(4, 7)$, $C(7, 6)$

18. $S(6, 5)$, $T(8, 3)$, $U(12, -1)$

19. $H(-8, 4)$, $I(-4, 2)$, $J(4, -2)$

20. $D(1, -5)$, $E(-3, 0)$, $F(-1, 0)$

Lesson 5-4

5-4 Practice

The Triangle Inequality

Determine whether the given measures can be the lengths of the sides of a triangle. Write *yes* or *no*.

1. 9, 12, 18

2. 8, 9, 17

3. 14, 14, 19

4. 23, 26, 50

5. 32, 41, 63

6. 2.7, 3.1, 4.3

7. 0.7, 1.4, 2.1

8. 12.3, 13.9, 25.2

Find the range for the measure of the third side of a triangle given the measures of two sides.

9. 6 and 19

10. 7 and 29

11. 13 and 27

12. 18 and 23

13. 25 and 38

14. 31 and 39

15. 42 and 6

16. 54 and 7

ALGEBRA Determine whether the given coordinates are the vertices of a triangle. Explain.

17. $R(1, 3), S(4, 0), T(10, -6)$

18. $W(2, 6), X(1, 6), Y(4, 2)$

19. $P(-3, 2), L(1, 1), M(9, -1)$

20. $B(1, 1), C(6, 5), D(4, -1)$

21. GARDENING Ha Poong has 4 lengths of wood from which he plans to make a border for a triangular-shaped herb garden. The lengths of the wood borders are 8 inches, 10 inches, 12 inches, and 18 inches. How many different triangular borders can Ha Poong make?

5-4 **Word Problem Practice**

The Triangle Inequality

1. **STICKS** Jamila has 5 sticks of lengths 2, 4, 6, 8, and 10 inches. Using three sticks at a time as the sides of triangles, how many triangles can she make?

Use the figure at the right for Exercises 2 and 3.

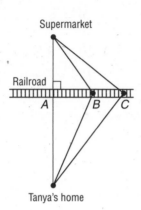

2. **PATHS** To get to the nearest supermarket, Tanya must walk over a railroad track. There are two places where she can cross the track (points A and B). Which path is longer? Explain.

3. **PATHS** While out walking one day Tanya finds a third place to cross the railroad tracks. Show that the path through point C is longer than the path through point B.

4. **CITIES** The distance between New York City and Boston is 187 miles and the distance between New York City and Hartford is 97 miles. Hartford, Boston, and New York City form a triangle on a map. What must the distance between Boston and Hartford be greater than?

TRIANGLES For Exercises 5–7, use the following information.

The figure shows an equilateral triangle *ABC* and a point *P* outside the triangle.

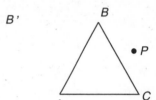

5. Draw the figure that is the result of turning the original figure 60° counterclockwise about *A*. Denote by *P′*, the image of *P* under this turn.

6. Note that $\overline{P'B}$ is congruent to $\overline{PC}$. It is also true that $\overline{PP'}$ is congruent to $\overline{PA}$. Why?

7. Show that $\overline{PA}, \overline{PB}$, and $\overline{PC}$ satisfy the triangle inequalities.

Lesson 5-4

5-4 Enrichment

Constructing Triangles

The measurements of the sides of a triangle are given. If a triangle having sides with these measurements is not possible, then write *impossible*. If a triangle is possible, draw it and measure each angle with a protractor.

1. $AR = 5$ cm $\quad$ $m\angle A =$

$\quad RT = 3$ cm $\quad$ $m\angle R =$

$\quad AT = 6$ cm $\quad$ $m\angle T =$

2. $PI = 8$ cm $\quad$ $m\angle P =$

$\quad IN = 3$ cm $\quad$ $m\angle I =$

$\quad PN = 2$ cm $\quad$ $m\angle N =$

3. $ON = 10$ cm $\quad$ $m\angle O =$

$\quad NE = 5.3$ cm $\quad$ $m\angle N =$

$\quad OE = 4.6$ cm $\quad$ $m\angle E =$

4. $TW = 6$ cm $\quad$ $m\angle T =$

$\quad WO = 7$ cm $\quad$ $m\angle W =$

$\quad TO = 2$ cm $\quad$ $m\angle O =$

5. $BA = 3.1$ cm $\quad$ $m\angle B =$

$\quad AT = 8$ cm $\quad$ $m\angle A =$

$\quad BT = 5$ cm $\quad$ $m\angle T =$

6. $AR = 4$ cm $\quad$ $m\angle A =$

$\quad RM = 5$ cm $\quad$ $m\angle R =$

$\quad AM = 3$ cm $\quad$ $m\angle M =$

5-5 Lesson Reading Guide

Inequalities Involving Two Triangles

Get Ready for the Lesson

Read the introduction to Lesson 5-5 in your textbook.

Suppose the thrill ride starts from the lowest position, rises to its highest position to the left, and then falls back to its lowest position. How many times will the arm make an angle of 20° with the vertical base?

Read the Lesson

1. Refer to the figure. Write a conclusion that you can draw from the given information. Then name the theorem that justifies your conclusion.

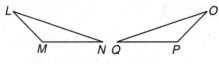

   a. $\overline{LM} \cong \overline{OP}$, $\overline{MN} \cong \overline{PQ}$, and $LN > OQ$

   b. $\overline{LM} \cong \overline{OP}$, $\overline{MN} \cong \overline{PQ}$, and $m\angle P < m\angle M$

   c. $LM = 8$, $LN = 15$, $OP = 8$, $OQ = 15$, $m\angle L = 22$, and $m\angle O = 21$

2. In the figure, $\triangle EFG$ is isosceles with base $\overline{FG}$ and F is the midpoint of $\overline{DG}$. Determine whether each of the following is a valid conclusion that you can draw based on the given information. (Write *valid* or *invalid*.) If the conclusion is valid, identify the definition, property, postulate, or theorem that supports it.

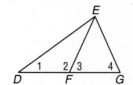

   a. $\angle 3 \cong \angle 4$

   b. $DF = GF$

   c. $\triangle DEF$ is isosceles.

   d. $m\angle 3 > m\angle 1$

   e. $m\angle 2 > m\angle 4$

   f. $m\angle 2 > m\angle 3$

   g. $DE > EG$

   h. $DE > FG$

Remember What You Learned

3. A good way to remember something is to think of it in concrete terms. How can you illustrate the Hinge Theorem with everyday objects?

Lesson 5-5

5-5 Study Guide and Intervention

Inequalities Involving Two Triangles

SAS Inequality The following theorem involves the relationship between the sides of two triangles and an angle in each triangle.

SAS Inequality/Hinge Theorem	If two sides of a triangle are congruent to two sides of another triangle and the included angle in one triangle has a greater measure than the included angle in the other, then the third side of the first triangle is longer than the third side of the second triangle.	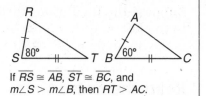 If $\overline{RS} \cong \overline{AB}$, $\overline{ST} \cong \overline{BC}$, and $m\angle S > m\angle B$, then $RT > AC$.

Example Write an inequality relating the lengths of $\overline{CD}$ and $\overline{AD}$.

Two sides of $\triangle BCD$ are congruent to two sides of $\triangle BAD$ and $m\angle CBD > m\angle ABD$. By the SAS Inequality/Hinge Theorem, $CD > AD$.

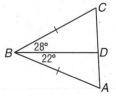

Exercises

Write an inequality relating the given pair of segment measures.

1.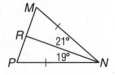

   MR, RP

2.

   AD, CD

3.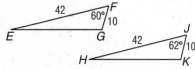

   EG, HK

4.

   MR, PR

Write an inequality to describe the possible values of x.

5.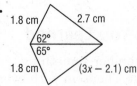

6.
   1.8 cm   2.7 cm
   62°
   65°
   1.8 cm $(3x - 2.1)$ cm

5-5 Study Guide and Intervention (continued)

Inequalities Involving Two Triangles

SSS Inequality The converse of the Hinge Theorem is also useful when two triangles have two pairs of congruent sides.

SSS Inequality	If two sides of a triangle are congruent to two sides of another triangle and the third side in one triangle is longer than the third side in the other, then the angle between the pair of congruent sides in the first triangle is greater than the corresponding angle in the second triangle.	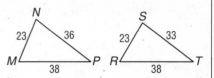 If $NM = SR$, $MP = RT$, and $NP > ST$, then $m\angle M > m\angle R$.

Example Write an inequality relating the measures of $\angle ABD$ and $\angle CBD$.

Two sides of $\triangle ABD$ are congruent to two sides of $\triangle CBD$, and $AD > CD$. By the SSS Inequality, $m\angle ABD > m\angle CBD$.

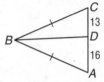

Exercises

Write an inequality relating the given pair of angle measures.

1.

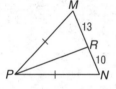

$m\angle MPR, m\angle NPR$

2.

$m\angle ABD, m\angle CBD$

3.

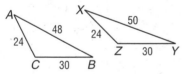

$m\angle C, m\angle Z$

4.

$m\angle XYW, m\angle WYZ$

Write an inequality to describe the possible values of x.

5.

6.

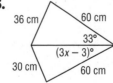

Lesson 5-5

5-5 Skills Practice

Inequalities Involving Two Triangles

Write an inequality relating the given pair of angles or segment measures.

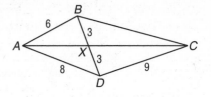

1. $m\angle BXA, m\angle DXA$

2. BC, DC

Write an inequality relating the given pair of angles or segment measures.

3. $m\angle STR, m\angle TRU$

4. PQ, RQ

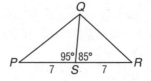

5. In the figure, $\overline{BA}, \overline{BD}, \overline{BC},$ and $\overline{BE}$ are congruent and $AC < DE$. How does $m\angle 1$ compare with $m\angle 3$? Explain your thinking.

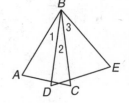

6. Write a two-column proof.
   Given: $\overline{BA} \cong \overline{DA}$
         $BC > DC$
   Prove: $m\angle 1 > m\angle 2$

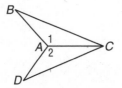

5-5 Practice

Inequalities Involving Two Triangles

Write an inequality relating the given pair of angles or segment measures.

1. AB, BK

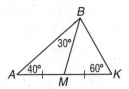

2. ST, SR

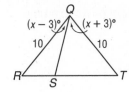

3. $m\angle CDF, m\angle EDF$

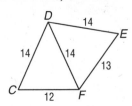

4. $m\angle R, m\angle T$

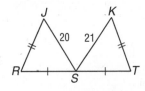

5. Write a two-column proof.
   Given: G is the midpoint of $\overline{DF}$.
        $m\angle 1 > m\angle 2$
   Prove: $ED > EF$

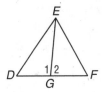

6. TOOLS Rebecca used a spring clamp to hold together a chair leg she repaired with wood glue. When she opened the clamp, she noticed that the angle between the handles of the clamp decreased as the distance between the handles of the clamp decreased. At the same time, the distance between the gripping ends of the clamp increased. When she released the handles, the distance between the gripping end of the clamp decreased and the distance between the handles increased. Is the clamp an example of the SAS or SSS Inequality?

Lesson 5-5

5-5 Word Problem Practice

Inequalities Involving Two Triangles

1. CLOCKS The minute hand of a grandfather clock is 3 feet long and the hour hand is 2 feet long. Is the distance between their ends greater at 3:00 or at 8:00?

2. FERRIS WHEEL A Ferris wheel has carriages located at the 10 vertices of a regular decagon.

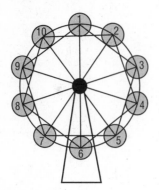

Which carriages are farther away from carriage number 1 than carriage number 4?

3. WALKWAY Tyree wants to make two slightly different triangles for his walkway. He has three pieces of wood to construct the frame of his triangles. After Tyree makes the first concrete triangle, he adjusts two sides of the triangle so that the angle they create is smaller than the angle in the first triangle. Explain how this changes the triangle.

4. MOUNTAIN PEAKS Emily lives the same distance from three mountain peaks: High Point, Topper, and Cloud Nine. For a photography class, Emily must take a photograph from her house that shows two of the mountain peaks. Which two peaks would she have the best chance of capturing in one image?

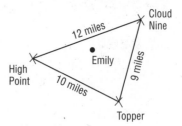

RUNNERS For Exercises 5 and 6, use the following information.

A photographer is taking pictures of three track stars, Amy, Noel, and Beth. The photographer stands on a track, which is shaped like a rectangle with semicircles on both ends.

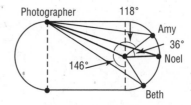

5. Based on the information in the figure, list the runners in order from nearest to farthest from the photographer.

6. Explain how to locate the point along the semicircular curve that the runners are on that is farthest away from the photographer.

5-5 Enrichment

Hinge Theorem

The Hinge Theorem that you studied in this section states that if two sides of a triangle are congruent to two sides of another triangle and the included angle in one triangle has a greater measure than the included angle in the other, then the third side of the first triangle is longer than the third side of the second triangle. In this activity, you will investigate whether the converse, inverse and contrapositive of the Hinge Theorem are also true.

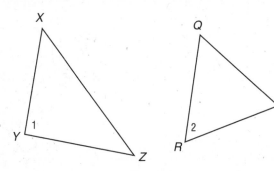

Hypothesis: $XY = QR$, $YZ = RS$, $m\angle 1 > m\angle 2$
Conclusion: $XZ > QS$

1. What is the converse of the Hinge Theorem?

2. Can you find any counterexamples to prove that the converse is false?

3. What is the inverse of the Hinge Theorem?

4. Can you find any counterexamples to prove that the inverse is false?

5. What is the contrapositive of the Hinge Theorem?

6. Can you find any counterexamples to prove that the contrapositive is false?

Lesson 5-5

5 Student Recording Sheet

Use this recording sheet with pages 314–315 of the Student Edition.

Read each question. Then fill in the correct answer.

1. Ⓐ Ⓑ Ⓒ Ⓓ

2. Ⓕ Ⓖ Ⓗ Ⓙ

3. Ⓐ Ⓑ Ⓒ Ⓓ

4. Ⓕ Ⓖ Ⓗ Ⓙ

5. Ⓐ Ⓑ Ⓒ Ⓓ

6. Record your answer and fill in the bubbles in the grid below. Be sure to use the correct place value.

7. Ⓕ Ⓖ Ⓗ Ⓙ

8. Ⓐ Ⓑ Ⓒ Ⓓ

9. Record your answer and fill in the bubbles in the grid below. Be sure to use the correct place value.

10. Ⓕ Ⓖ Ⓗ Ⓙ

11. Ⓐ Ⓑ Ⓒ Ⓓ

12. Ⓕ Ⓖ Ⓗ Ⓙ

Pre-AP

Record your answers for Question 13 on the back of this paper.

Assessment

5 **Rubric for Scoring Pre-AP**

(Use to score the Pre-AP question on page 315 of the Student Edition.)

General Scoring Guidelines

• If a student gives only a correct numerical answer to a problem but does not show how he or she arrived at the answer, the student will be awarded only 1 credit. All extended-response questions require the student to show work.

• A fully correct answer for a multiple-part question requires correct responses for all parts of the question. For example, if a question has three parts, the correct response to one or two parts of the question that required work to be shown is *not* considered a fully correct response.

• Students who use trial and error to solve a problem must show their method. Merely showing that the answer checks or is correct is not considered a complete response for full credit.

Exercise 13 Rubric

Score	Specific Criteria
4	Triangle ABC is graphed correctly with vertices $A(-3, 1)$, $B(0, -2)$, and $C(3, 4)$. The distance formula is used correctly to show that $AB = 4.2$, $BC = 6.7$, and $AC = 6.7$. The information in part b shows that triangle ABC is isosceles because $BC = AC$. To prove that $\angle A \cong \angle B$, the student shows that according to the Isosceles Triangle Theorem, if two sides of a triangle are congruent, then the angles opposite those sides are congruent. To prove that $m\angle A > m\angle C$, the student shows that if one side of a triangle is longer than another side, the angle opposite the longer side has a greater measure than the angle opposite the shorter side. Since BC is greater than AB, $m\angle A > m\angle C$.
3	A generally correct solution, but may contain minor flaws in reasoning or computation.
2	A partially correct interpretation and/or solution to the problem.
1	A correct solution with no evidence or explanation.
0	An incorrect solution indicating no mathematical understanding of the concept or task, or no solution is given.

5 **Chapter 5 Quiz 1**

(Lessons 5–1 and 5–2)

SCORE _____

1. What is the point called where the perpendicular bisectors of the sides of a triangle intersect?

1._____

2. Determine which angle has the greatest measure.

2._____

3. What is the name of the point that is two-thirds of the way from each vertex of a triangle to the midpoint of the opposite side?

3._____

4. If $\overline{CD}$ is the perpendicular bisector of $\overline{AB}$ and $\overline{AB}$ is the perpendicular bisector of $\overline{CD}$, find x.

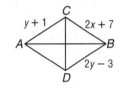

4._____

5. Find the shortest segment.

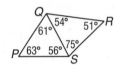

5._____

---

5 **Chapter 5 Quiz 2**

(Lesson 5–3)

SCORE _____

1. What do you assume in an indirect proof?

1._____

For Questions 2 and 3, write the assumption you would make to start an indirect proof of each statement.

2. If $2x + 7 = 19$, then $x = 6$.

2._____

3. If $\triangle ABC$ is isosceles with base $\overline{AC}$, then $\overline{AB} \cong \overline{BC}$.

3._____

For Questions 4 and 5, write the assumption you would make to start an indirect proof.

4. **Given:** $3x - 10 > 20$
   Prove: $x > 10$

4._____

5. **Given:** $\overline{CD}$ is not a median of $\triangle ABC$.
   $\angle 1 \cong \angle 2$
   Prove: $\overline{CB} \not\cong \overline{CA}$

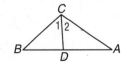

5._____

5 **Chapter 5 Quiz 3**

SCORE _____

(Lesson 5–4)

1. Write *AB*, *AC*, and *AD* in order from least to greatest measure.

1. _____

2. Determine whether *A*(2, 3), *B*(7, 12), *C*(−5, −24) are the vertices of △*ABC*. Explain.

2. _____

3. Name the shortest distance from *A* to $\overline{BC}$.

3. _____

4. Write an inequality to describe the possible values of *x*.

4. _____

5. MULTIPLE CHOICE Which of the following sets of numbers can be the lengths of the sides of a triangle?

A. 5, 5, 10   **B.** $\sqrt{39}$, $\sqrt{8}$, $\sqrt{5}$ **C.** 2.5, 3.4, 4.6   **D.** 1, 2, 4

5. _____

- -

5 **Chapter 5 Quiz 4**

SCORE _____

(Lesson 5–5)

1. Write an inequality relating *m*∠1 to *m*∠2.

1. _____

2. Write an inequality relating *AB* to *DE*.

2. _____

3. Write an inequality about the length of $\overline{GH}$.

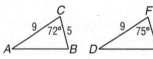

3. _____

For Questions 4 and 5, complete the proof by supplying the missing information for each corresponding location.

Given: △*ACE*, *AB* = *DE*, and *BE* > *AD*
Prove: *m*∠*CAE* > *m*∠*CEA*

Statements	Reasons
1. *AB* = *DE*, *BE* > *AD*	1. Given
2. $\overline{AB} \cong \overline{DE}$	2. Def. of ≅ segments
3. (Question 4)	3. Reflexive Prop.
4. *m*∠*CAE* > *m*∠*CEA*	4. (Question 5)

4. _____

5. _____

5 Chapter 5 Mid-Chapter Test

(Lessons 5–1 through 5–3)

SCORE _____

Part I *Write the letter for the correct answer in the blank at the right of each question.*

1. Which of the following can intersect outside a triangle?

   A. angle bisectors   **C.** altitudes

   B. medians   **D.** sides

   1. _____

2. What is the name of the point of concurrency of the altitudes of a triangle?

   F. orthocenter   **H.** incenter

   G. circumcenter   **J.** centroid

   2. _____

3. What is the name of the point of concurrency of the medians of a triangle?

   A. orthocenter   **C.** incenter

   B. circumcenter   **D.** centroid

   3. _____

4. Name the longest segment.

   F. $\overline{BD}$ **H.** $\overline{AD}$

   G. $\overline{BC}$ **J.** $\overline{CD}$

   4. _____

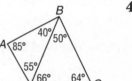

5. $\overline{PS}$ is the perpendicular bisector of $\overline{QR}$ and $\overline{QR}$ is the perpendicular bisector of $\overline{PS}$. If $PQ = 2x + 9$ and $QS = 5x - 12$, find x.

   A. 2   **B.** 3   **C.** 5   **D.** 7

   5. _____

Part II

6. Write an inequality to describe the possible values of x.

   6. _____

7. State the assumptions you would make to start an indirect proof of the statement *If $x > 2$, then $x^2 > 4$.*

   7. _____

8. An advertising company is designing a corporate flag in the shape of an isosceles triangle. The right-hand edge of the company logo will be placed at the centroid, L, of the $\triangle ABC$. The length of the altitude CD is 24 inches. How far is the right-hand edge of the logo from the vertex C?

   8. _____

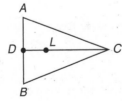

9. Write the assumption you would make to start an indirect proof.

   Given: $\overline{BD}$ is not a median of $\triangle ABC$.

        $\angle 1 \cong \angle 2$

   Prove: $\overline{BD}$ does not bisect $\angle ABC$.

   9. _____

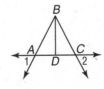

5 · Chapter 5 Vocabulary Test

SCORE _____

altitude	incenter	orthocenter
centroid	indirect proof	perpendicular bisector
circumcenter	indirect reasoning	point of concurrency
concurrent lines	median	proof by contradiction

State whether each sentence is *true* or *false*. If false, replace the underlined word or number to make a true sentence.

1. The altitude of a triangle is a segment whose endpoints are a vertex of a triangle and the midpoint of the side opposite the vertex.

1. _____

2. The centroid of a triangle is the point where the altitudes of the triangle intersect.

2. _____

Choose the correct term to complete each sentence.

3. The point of concurrency of the perpendicular bisectors of a triangle is called the (*circumcenter* or *median*).

3. _____

4. The (*incenter* or *orthocenter*) of a triangle is the intersection of the angle bisectors of the triangle.

4. _____

5. The sum of the measures of any two sides of a triangle is (*greater* or *less*) than the measure of the third side.

5. _____

Choose from the terms above to complete each sentence.

6. A(n) _____ is a segment that joins a vertex of a triangle and is perpendicular to the side opposite to the vertex.

6. _____

7. Proof by contradiction is a type of _____.

7. _____

8. The _____ of a triangle is equidistant from the vertices of the triangle.

8. _____

Define each term in your own words.

9. *concurrent lines*

9. _____

10. *median*

10. _____

5 Chapter 5 Test, Form 1

Write the letter for the correct answer in the blank at the right of each question.

For Questions 1–4, refer to the figure at the right.

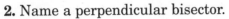

1. Name an altitude.
   - **A.** $\overline{DE}$
   - **C.** $\overleftrightarrow{GB}$
   - **B.** $\overline{AB}$
   - **D.** $\overrightarrow{CF}$

   1. _____

2. Name a perpendicular bisector.
   - **F.** $\overline{DE}$
   - **G.** $\overline{AB}$
   - **H.** $\overleftrightarrow{GB}$
   - **J.** $\overrightarrow{CF}$

   2. _____

3. Name an angle bisector.
   - **A.** $\overline{DE}$
   - **B.** $\overline{AB}$
   - **C.** $\overleftrightarrow{GB}$
   - **D.** $\overrightarrow{CF}$

   3. _____

4. Name a median.
   - **F.** $\overline{DE}$
   - **G.** $\overline{AB}$
   - **H.** $\overleftrightarrow{GB}$
   - **J.** $\overrightarrow{CF}$

   4. _____

For Questions 5–7, refer to the figure to determine which is a true statement for the given information.

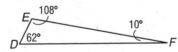

5. $\overline{AC}$ is a median.
   - **A.** $m\angle ACD = 90$
   - **C.** $BC = CD$
   - **B.** $\angle BAC \cong \angle DAC$
   - **D.** $\angle B \cong \angle D$

   5. _____

6. $\overline{AC}$ is an angle bisector.
   - **F.** $m\angle ACD = 90$
   - **G.** $\angle BAC \cong \angle DAC$
   - **H.** $BC = CD$
   - **J.** $\angle B \cong \angle D$

   6. _____

7. $\overline{AC}$ is an altitude.
   - **A.** $m\angle ACD = 90$
   - **B.** $\angle BAC \cong \angle DAC$
   - **C.** $BC = CD$
   - **D.** $\angle B \cong \angle D$

   7. _____

8. Name the longest side of $\triangle DEF$.
   - **F.** $\overline{DE}$
   - **H.** $\overline{DF}$
   - **G.** $\overline{EF}$
   - **J.** cannot tell

   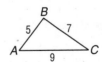

   8. _____

9. Which angle in $\triangle ABC$ has the greatest measure?
   - **A.** $\angle A$
   - **C.** $\angle C$
   - **B.** $\angle B$
   - **D.** cannot tell

   9. _____

10. What is the converse of the SAS Inequality Theorem?
    - **F.** Hinge Theorem
    - **G.** SSS Inequality Theorem
    - **H.** Exterior Angle Inequality Theorem
    - **J.** Triangle Inequality Theorem

    10. _____

11. Which assumption would you make to indirectly prove $x > 5$?
    - **A.** $x < 5$
    - **B.** $x \le 5$
    - **C.** $x = 5$
    - **D.** $x > 5$

    11. _____

Assessment

12. Find the possible values for $m\angle 1$.

    F. $180 > m\angle 1 > 62$ **H.** $0 < m\angle 1 < 62$

    G. $90 > m\angle 1 > 62$ **J.** $m\angle 1 = 118$

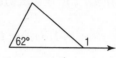

12. _____

13. Find x.

    A. 5   **C.** 10

    B. 7   **D.** 15

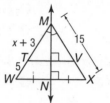

13. _____

14. If D is the circumcenter of $\triangle ABC$ and $AD = 6$, find BD.

    F. 4   **H.** 9

    G. 6   **J.** 12

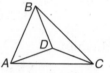

14. _____

15. Choose the assumption you would make to start an indirect proof of $x > 3$.

    A. $x < 3$ **B.** $x \geq 3$ **C.** $x \leq 3$ **D.** $x = 3$

15. _____

16. Choose the assumption you would make to start an indirect proof.

    Given: $a \nparallel b$ **Prove:** $\angle 1$ and $\angle 2$ are not supplementary.

    F. $a \parallel b$ **H.** $\angle 1 \cong \angle 2$

    G. $\angle 1$ and $\angle 2$ are supplementary.   **J.** $\angle 1$ and $\angle 2$ are complementary.

16. _____

17. Which of the following sets of numbers can be the lengths of the sides of a triangle?

    A. 12, 9, 4   **B.** 1, 2, 3   **C.** 5, 5, 10   **D.** $\sqrt{2}, \sqrt{5}, \sqrt{18}$

17. _____

18. Find the shortest distance from B to $\overline{AC}$.

    F. BD **H.** BF

    G. BC **J.** BE

18. _____

For Questions 19 and 20, refer to the figures.

19. **Given:** $\overline{AC} \cong \overline{DF}, \overline{AB} \cong \overline{DE}, m\angle A > m\angle D$

    Which can be concluded by the SAS Inequality Theorem?

    A. $\triangle ABC \cong \triangle DEF$ **C.** $BC < EF$

    B. $BC = EF$ **D.** $BC > EF$

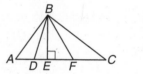

19. _____

20. **Given:** $\overline{AB} \cong \overline{DE}, \overline{BC} \cong \overline{EF}, AC < DF$

    Which can be concluded by the SSS Inequality Theorem?

    F. $m\angle B < m\angle E$ **H.** $m\angle B = m\angle E$

    G. $m\angle B > m\angle E$ **J.** $\triangle BAC \cong \triangle EDF$

20. _____

Bonus $\overline{QS}$ is a median of $\triangle PQR$ with point S on $\overline{PR}$.
If $PS = x^2 - 3x$ and $SR = 2x + 6$, find x.

B:

5 **Chapter 5 Test, Form 2A**

Write the letter for the correct answer in the blank at the right of each question.

For Questions 1–4, refer to the figure.

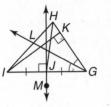

1. Name an angle bisector.
   A. $\overline{KI}$　　　**B.** $\overrightarrow{GL}$　　　**C.** $\overrightarrow{JM}$　　　**D.** $\overline{HJ}$

1. _____

2. Name a median.
   F. $\overline{KI}$　　　**G.** $\overrightarrow{GL}$　　　**H.** $\overrightarrow{JM}$　　　**J.** $\overline{HJ}$

2. _____

3. Name an altitude.
   A. $\overline{KI}$　　　**B.** $\overline{GL}$　　　**C.** $\overrightarrow{JM}$　　　**D.** $\overline{HJ}$

3. _____

4. Name a perpendicular bisector.
   F. $\overline{KI}$　　　**G.** $\overrightarrow{GL}$　　　**H.** $\overrightarrow{JM}$　　　**J.** $\overline{HJ}$

4. _____

For Questions 5–7, refer to the figure to determine which is a true statement for the given information.

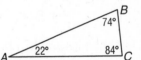

5. $\overline{YW}$ is an angle bisector.
   A. $\angle YWZ$ is a right angle.　　　**C.** $XW = WZ$
   B. $\angle XYW \cong \angle ZYW$　　　　　**D.** $XY = ZY$

5. _____

6. $\overline{YW}$ is an altitude.
   F. $\angle YWZ$ is a right angle.　　　**H.** $XW = WZ$
   G. $\angle XYW \cong \angle ZYW$　　　　　**J.** $XY = ZY$

6. _____

7. $\overline{YW}$ is a median.
   A. $\angle YWZ$ is a right angle.　　　**C.** $XW = WZ$
   B. $\angle XYW \cong \angle ZYW$　　　　　**D.** $XY = ZY$

7. _____

8. Name the longest side of $\triangle ABC$.
   F. $\overline{AB}$　　　　　　　　　　**H.** $\overline{AC}$
   G. $\overline{BC}$　　　　　　　　　　**J.** cannot tell

8. _____

9. Name the angle with greatest measure in $\triangle DEF$.
   A. $\angle D$　　　　　　　　　　**C.** $\angle F$
   B. $\angle E$　　　　　　　　　　**D.** cannot tell

9. _____

10. Which theorem compares the sides of the same triangle?
    F. SAS Inequality Theorem.　　　**H.** Exterior Angle Inequality Theorem
    G. SSS Inequality Theorem　　　　**J.** Triangle Inequality Theorem

10. _____

11. Tisha wants to plant a garden in the widest corner of her triangular backyard. The backyard is bordered by the back of the house that is 50 feet long, fence A that is 27 feet long, and fence B that is 35 feet long. Which corner has the widest measure?
    A. corner between fences A and B
    B. All three corners have the same measure
    C. corner between the back of the house and fence A
    D. corner between the back of the house and fence B

11. _____

12. Find the possible values for $m\angle 1$.   12._____

    F. $90 > m\angle 1 > 74$

    G. $180 > m\angle 1 > 74$

    H. $0 < m\angle 1 < 74$

    J. $m\angle 1 = 106$

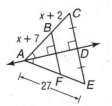

13. Find x.   13._____

    A. 9

    B. 11

    C. 27

    D. 32

14. Which is another name for an indirect proof?   14._____

    F. proof by deduction

    G. proof by converse

    H. proof by inverse

    J. proof by contradiction

15. Choose the assumption you would make to start an indirect proof of $x < 2$.   15._____

    A. $x > 2$ **B.** $x \geq 2$ **C.** $x = 2$ **D.** $x \leq 2$

16. Choose the assumption you would make to start an indirect proof.   16._____

    Given: $\angle 1$ is an exterior angle of $\triangle ABC$. **Prove:** $m\angle 1 = m\angle B + m\angle C$

    F. $\angle 1$ is not an exterior angle of $\triangle ABE$.

    G. $\angle 1$ is an interior angle of $\triangle ABC$.

    H. $m\angle 1 \neq m\angle B + m\angle C$

    J. $m\angle 1 = m\angle B$

17. Which of the following sets of numbers can be the lengths of the sides of a triangle?   17._____

    A. 6, 6, 12   **B.** 6, 7, 13   **C.** $\sqrt{2}, \sqrt{5}, \sqrt{15}$ **D.** 2.6, 8.1, 10.2

18. What is the relationship between the lengths of QS and RS?   18._____

    F. $QS = RS$

    G. $QS < RS$

    H. $QS > RS$

    J. cannot tell

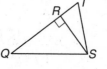

19. What is the relationship between the lengths of DC and AD?   19._____

    A. $DC < AD$

    B. $DC > AD$

    C. $DC = AD$

    D. cannot tell

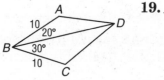

20. What is the relationship between the measures of $\angle 1$ and $\angle 2$?   20._____

    F. $m\angle 1 = m\angle 2$

    G. $m\angle 1 < m\angle 2$

    H. $m\angle 1 > m\angle 2$

    J. cannot tell

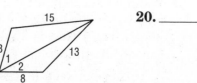

Bonus $\overline{YW}$ bisects $\angle XYZ$ in $\triangle XYZ$. Point W is on $\overline{XZ}$.   **B:** _____

    If $m\angle XYW = 2x + 18$ and $m\angle ZYW = x^2 - 5x$, find x.

5 **Chapter 5 Test, Form 2B**

SCORE _____

Write the letter for the correct answer in the blank at the right of each question.

For Questions 1–4, refer to the figure.

1. Name a median.
   A. $\overline{RW}$ C. $\overline{QT}$
   B. $\overleftrightarrow{SV}$ D. $\overrightarrow{RU}$

1. _____

2. Name an angle bisector.
   F. $\overline{RW}$ G. $\overleftrightarrow{SV}$ H. $\overline{QT}$ J. $\overrightarrow{RU}$

2. _____

3. Name a perpendicular bisector.
   A. $\overline{RW}$ B. $\overleftrightarrow{SV}$ C. $\overline{QT}$ D. $\overrightarrow{RU}$

3. _____

4. Name an altitude.
   F. $\overline{RW}$ G. $\overline{RP}$ H. $\overline{QT}$ J. $\overrightarrow{RU}$

4. _____

For Questions 5–7, refer to the figure to determine which is a true statement for the given information.

5. $\overline{FG}$ is an altitude.
   A. $\angle DGF$ is a right angle.   C. $DG = GE$
   B. $DF = EF$ D. $\angle DFG \cong \angle EFG$

5. _____

6. $\overline{FG}$ is a median.
   F. $\angle DGF$ is a right angle.   H. $DG = GE$
   G. $DF = EF$ J. $\angle DFG \cong \angle EFG$

6. _____

7. $\overline{FG}$ is an angle bisector.
   A. $\angle DGF$ is a right angle.   C. $DG = GE$
   B. $DF = EF$ D. $\angle DFG \cong \angle EFG$

7. _____

8. Name the longest side of $\triangle ABC$.
   F. $\overline{AB}$ H. $\overline{AC}$
   G. $\overline{BC}$ J. cannot tell

8. _____

9. Name the angle with the greatest measure in $\triangle GHI$.
   A. $\angle G$ C. $\angle I$
   B. $\angle H$ D. cannot tell

9. _____

10. Two sides of a triangle are congruent to two sides of another triangle and the included angle in the first triangle has a greater measure than the included angle in the second triangle. These are the assumptions of which theorem
    F. SAS Inequality Theorem   H. Exterior Angle Inequality Theorem
    G. SSS Inequality Theorem   J. Triangle Inequality Theorem

10. _____

Assessment

11. Carrie, Maria, and Nayla are friends that live close to one another. Which two friends have the shortest distance between them?

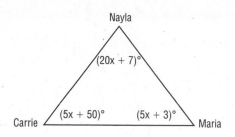

A. Maria and Nayla
B. Carrie and Maria
C. Carrie and Nayla
D. All three live equal distances from each other.

11._____

12. Find the possible values for $m\angle 1$.

F. $m\angle 1 = 124$ H. $90 > m\angle 1 > 56$
G. $0 < m\angle 1 < 56$ J. $180 > m\angle 1 > 56$

12._____

13. Find ST.

A. 12   C. 23
B. 18   D. 24

13._____

14. Which of the following is the last step in an indirect proof?

F. show the assumption true   H. show the conclusion false
G. show the assumption false   J. contradict the conclusion

14._____

15. Choose the assumption you would make to start an indirect proof of $x \leq 1$.

A. $x > 1$ B. $x = 1$ C. $x < 1$ D. $x \leq 1$

15._____

16. Choose the assumption you would make to start this indirect proof.

Given: $\overline{AB}$ bisects $\angle CAD$.
Prove: $\angle ACB \not\cong \angle DAB$

F. $\overline{AB}$ does not bisect $\angle CAD$.   H. $\overline{AB}$ is a median.
G. $\triangle ACD$ is isosceles.   J. $\angle ACB \cong \angle DAB$

16._____

17. Which of the following sets of numbers can be the lengths of the sides of a triangle?

A. 12, 9, 2   B. 11, 12, 23   C. 2, 3, 4   D. $\sqrt{3}, \sqrt{5}, \sqrt{18}$

17._____

18. What is the relationship between the lengths of YW and YX?

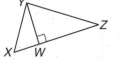

F. $YW = YX$ H. $YW > YX$
G. $YW < YX$ J. cannot tell

18._____

19. What is the relationship between the lengths of DG and GF?

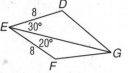

A. $DG > GF$ C. $DG = GF$
B. $DG < GF$ D. cannot tell

19._____

20. What is the relationship between the measures of $\angle 1$ and $\angle 2$?

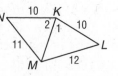

F. $m\angle 1 = m\angle 2$ H. $m\angle 1 > m\angle 2$
G. $m\angle 1 < m\angle 2$ J. cannot tell

20._____

Bonus $\overline{HJ}$ is an altitude of $\triangle GHI$ with point J on $\overline{GI}$.
If $m\angle GJH = 5x + 30$, $GH = 3x + 4$, $HI = 5x - 3$,
$JI = 4x - 3$, and $GJ = x + 6$, find the perimeter of $\triangle GHI$.

B: _____

5 **Chapter 5 Test, Form 2C**

SCORE _____

1. Name an angle bisector.

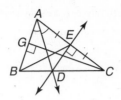

1. _____

2. The perimeter of $ABCD$ is 44. Find x. Then describe the relationship between $\overleftrightarrow{AC}$ and $\overline{BD}$.

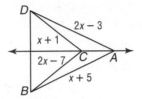

2. _____

3. If point E is the centroid of $\triangle ABC$, $BD = 12$, $EF = 7$, and $AG = 15$, find ED.

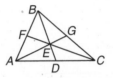

3. _____

4. The vertices of $\triangle XYZ$ are $X(-2, 6)$, $Y(4, 10)$, and $Z(14, 6)$. Find the coordinates of the centroid of $\triangle XYZ$.

4. _____

5. If $\overline{PO}$ is an angle bisector of $\angle MON$, find x.

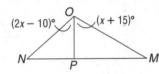

5. _____

6. A biker will jump over a ramp, where x and z are measured in feet. Write an inequality relating x and z.

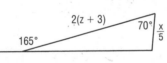

6. _____

7. List the angles of $\triangle GHI$ in order from least to greatest measure.

7. _____

8. List the sides of $\triangle PQR$ in order from shortest to longest.

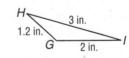

8. _____

9. Find the shortest segment.

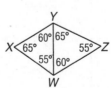

9. _____

10. Write the assumption you would make to start an indirect proof of the statement *If 16 is a factor of n, then 4 is a factor of n.*

10. _____

11. Write the assumption you would make to start an indirect proof of the statement *If $\overline{AB}$ is an altitude of equilateral triangle ABC, then $\overline{AB}$ is a median.*

11. _____

Assessment

5   **Chapter 5 Test, Form 2C** *(continued)*

12. Write the assumption you would make to start an indirect proof for the following.

Given: $\overline{XY} \not\cong \overline{YZ}$
$\overline{YW}$ bisects $\angle XYZ$.
Prove: $\angle X \not\cong \angle Z$

12. _____

13. The measures of two sides of a triangle are 10 meters and 23 meters. If the measure of the third side is x meters, find the range for x.

13. _____

14. Find the shortest distance from P to $\overrightarrow{RQ}$.

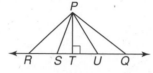

14. _____

15. If $\overrightarrow{BD}$ bisects $\angle ABC$, find x.

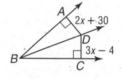

15. _____

16. Write an inequality to compare EF and GH.

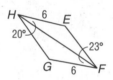

16. _____

17. Write an inequality to compare $m\angle 1$ and $m\angle 2$.

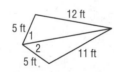

17. _____

For Questions 18–20, complete the proof below by supplying the missing information for each corresponding location.

Given: $\triangle ABC$, $AD = CB$, and $AC > DB$
Prove: $m\angle ADC > m\angle DCB$

Statements	Reasons
1. $AD = CB$ and $AC > DB$	1. Given
2. $\overline{AD} \cong \overline{CB}$	2. (Question 18)
3. $\overline{CD} \cong \overline{CD}$	3. (Question 19)
4. $m\angle ADC > m\angle DCB$	4. (Question 20)

18. _____

19. _____

20. _____

Bonus Write an equation in slope-intercept form for the altitude to $\overline{BC}$.

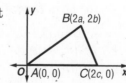

B: _____

5 **Chapter 5 Test, Form 2D**

1. Name a perpendicular bisector.

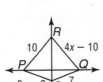

1. _____

2. The perimeter of *PRQS* is 34. Find *x*. Then describe the relationship between $\overleftrightarrow{RS}$ and $\overline{PQ}$.

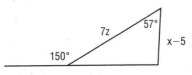

2. _____

3. If point *N* is the centroid of △*HIJ*, *IM* = 18, *KN* = 4, and *HL* = 15, find *JN*.

3. _____

4. The vertices of △*DEF* are *D*(4, 12), *E*(14, 6), and *F*(−6, 2). Find the coordinates of the circumcenter of △*DEF*.

4. _____

5. If $\overline{RU}$ is an altitude for △*RST*, find *x*.

5. _____

6. A rubber doorstop has a hypotenuse measuring 7*z* and a height measuring *x* − 5. Write an inequality relating *x* and *z*.

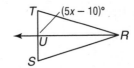

6. _____

7. List the angles of △*TUV* in order from least to greatest measure.

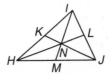

7. _____

8. List the sides of △*FGH* in order from shortest to longest.

8. _____

9. Name the longest segment.

9. _____

10. Write the assumption you would make to start an indirect proof of the statement *If n is an even number, then n² is an even number.*

10. _____

11. Write the assumption you would make to start an indirect proof of the statement *If $\overline{AD}$ is an angle bisector of equilateral triangle ABC, then $\overline{AD}$ is an altitude.*

11. _____

5 **Chapter 5 Test, Form 2D** *(continued)*

12. Write the assumption you would make to start an indirect proof for the following.

   Given: V is not the midpoint of $\overline{PQ}$;
   $\angle P \cong \angle Q$.
   Prove: $\overline{SV} \not\perp \overline{PQ}$

12. _____

13. The measures of two sides of a triangle are 14 feet and 29 feet. If the measure of the third side is x meters, find the range for x.

13. _____

14. Find the shortest distance from B to $\overleftrightarrow{AC}$.

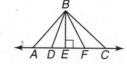

14. _____

15. If $\overrightarrow{YW}$ bisects $\angle XYZ$, find x.

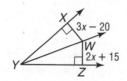

15. _____

16. Write an inequality relating $m\angle 1$ and $m\angle 2$.

16. _____

17. Write an inequality relating BC and ED.

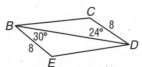

17. _____

For Questions 18–20, complete the proof below by supplying the missing information for each corresponding location.

Given: K is the midpoint of $\overline{AB}$.
   $m\angle MKB < m\angle MKA$
Prove: $MB < AM$

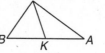

Statements	Reasons
1. K is the midpoint of $\overline{AB}$; $m\angle MKB < m\angle MKA$.	1. Given
2. $\overline{BK} \cong \overline{KA}$	2. (Question 18)
3. $\overline{MK} \cong \overline{MK}$	3. (Question 19)
4. $MB < AM$	4. (Question 20)

18. _____

19. _____

20. _____

Bonus Write an equation in slope-intercept form for the perpendicular bisector of $\overline{CE}$.

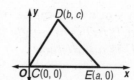

B: _____

Assessment

1. If point G is the centroid of $\triangle ABC$, $AE = 24$, $DG = 5$, and $CG = 14$, find DB.

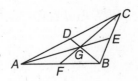

1. _____

2. The vertices of $\triangle EFG$ are $E(2, 4)$, $F(10, -6)$, and $G(-4, -8)$. Find the coordinates of the orthocenter of $\triangle EFG$.

2. _____

3. If $\overline{JL}$ is a median for $\triangle IJK$, find x.

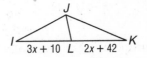

3. _____

4. Write a compound inequality for the possible measures of $\angle L$.

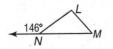

4. _____

5. List the angles of $\triangle GHI$ in order from least to greatest measure.

5. _____

6. List the sides of $\triangle PQR$ in order from shortest to longest.

6. _____

7. Name the shortest and the longest segments.

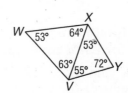

7. _____

8. Write the assumption you would make to begin an indirect proof of the statement *If $2x + 6 = 12$, then $x = 3$.*

8. _____

9. Determine whether 8, 4, and 2 can be the lengths of the sides of a triangle. Write *yes* or *no*. Explain.

9. _____

10. Write the assumption you would make to begin an indirect proof of the statement *The three angle bisectors of a triangle are concurrent.*

10. _____

11. Write and solve an inequality for x.

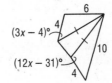

11. _____

5 **Chapter 5 Test, Form 3** *(continued)*

12. If $\overline{FH}$ is a median of $\triangle EFG$, find the perimeter of $\triangle EFG$.

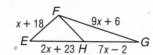

12. _____

13. Write the assumption you would make to start an indirect proof for the following.

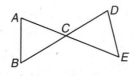

Given: $\overline{AB} \not\cong \overline{DE}$ and $\overline{AC} \cong \overline{CD}$
Prove: $\angle B \not\cong \angle E$

13. _____

14. The measures of two sides of a triangle are 24 inches and 29 inches. If the measure of the third side is x inches, find the range for x.

14. _____

15. Name the shortest distance from Y to $\overleftrightarrow{XZ}$.

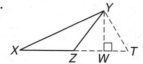

15. _____

16. Write and solve an inequality for x.

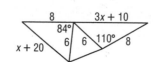

16. _____

For Questions 17–20, complete the proof below by supplying the missing information for each corresponding location.

Given: $XW = YZ$, $XK > WK$, and $KZ > KY$
Prove: $m\angle XWZ > m\angle YZW$

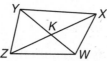

Statements	Reasons
1. $XW = YZ$, $XK > WK$, and $KZ > KY$	1. Given
2. $XW \cong YZ$	2. (Question 17)
3. $XZ > WY$	3. (Question 18)
4. $WZ \cong WZ$	4. (Question 19)
5. $m\angle XWZ > m\angle YZW$	5. (Question 20)

17. _____

18. _____

19. _____

20. _____

Bonus Write an equation in slope-intercept form for the line containing the median to $\overline{DE}$.

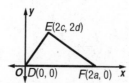

B: _____

5 Chapter 5 Extended-Response Test

Demonstrate your knowledge by giving a clear, concise solution to each problem. Be sure to include all relevant drawings and justify your answers. You may show your solution in more than one way or investigate beyond the requirements of the problem.

1. Two sticks are bent and connected with a rubber band as shown in the diagram. Describe what happens to the rubber band as the ends of the sticks are pulled farther apart. Name the theorem this situation illustrates.

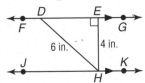

2. Mary says $\overleftrightarrow{FG}$ and $\overleftrightarrow{JK}$ are six inches apart and Ashley says they are four inches apart. Who is correct? Explain your answer.

3. Suppose $\overline{BD}$ is drawn on this figure so that point D is on $\overrightarrow{AC}$ and has a length of 6 centimeters. If the shortest distance from B to $\overrightarrow{AC}$ is 5 centimeters, in how many different places on $\overrightarrow{AC}$ could point D be located? Explain.

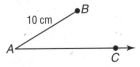

4. Draw a triangle that satisfies each situation.

   a. Two of the sides are altitudes.

   b. The altitudes intersect outside the triangle.

   c. The altitudes intersect inside the triangle.

   d. The altitudes are also the medians of the triangle.

5 **Standardized Test Practice**

(Chapters 1–5)

Part 1: Multiple Choice

Instructions: Fill in the appropriate circle for the best answer.

1. If ∠*BXY* is a right angle, then which statements are true? (Lesson 1–4)   1. Ⓐ Ⓑ Ⓒ Ⓓ

   I $m\angle BXY = 90$

   II The measure of an angle vertical to ∠*BXY* would be 90.

   III The measure of an angle supplementary to ∠*BXY* would be 90.

   A I only   **B** I and III   **C** I, II, and III   **D** I and II

2. Which is the contrapositive of the conditional statement   2. Ⓕ Ⓖ Ⓗ Ⓙ
   If $m\angle K = 45$, *then* $x = 5$? (Lesson 2-3)

   F If $m\angle K \neq 45$, then $x \neq 5$ **H** If $x = 5$, then $m\angle K = 45$

   G If $x \neq 5$, then $m\angle K \neq 45$ **J** If $m\angle K \neq 45$, then $x = 5$

3. Find $m\angle HJK$. (Lesson 3-2)   3. Ⓐ Ⓑ Ⓒ Ⓓ

   A 33   **C** 78

   B 45   **D** 147

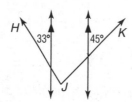

4. The line $y - 5 = -x + 3$ satisfies which conditions? (Lesson 3-4)   4. Ⓕ Ⓖ Ⓗ Ⓙ

   F $m = -1$, contains $(-5, 3)$ **H** $m = -1$, contains $(5, 3)$

   G $m = 1$, contains $(-5, -3)$ **J** $m = -1$, contains $(5, -3)$

5. Given $D(0, 4)$, $E(2, 4)$, $F(2, 1)$, $A(0, 2)$, and $C(-2, -1)$, which   5. Ⓐ Ⓑ Ⓒ Ⓓ
   coordinates for B would make $\triangle ABC \cong \triangle DEF$? (Lesson 4-4)

   A $B(-2, 2)$ **C** $B(0, 0)$

   B $B(0, 1)$ **D** $B(-1, 0)$

6. In $\triangle XYZ$, which type of line is ℓ? (Lesson 5-1)   6. Ⓕ Ⓖ Ⓗ Ⓙ

   F perpendicular bisector

   G angle bisector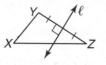

   H altitude

   J median

7. Which assumption would you make to start an indirect proof of   7. Ⓐ Ⓑ Ⓒ Ⓓ
   the statement *If* $2x - 5 < 17$, *then* $x < 11$? (Lesson 5-3)

   A $x < 11$ **B** $x \geq 11$ **C** $x > 11$ **D** $x \neq 11$

8. Which inequality describes the possible   8. Ⓕ Ⓖ Ⓗ Ⓙ
   values of x? (Lesson 5-5)

   F $x > 6$ **H** $x \not< 12$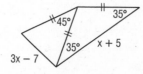

   G $x < 6$ **J** $6 < x < 12$

5 Standardized Test Practice (continued)

For Questions 9–11 refer to the figure.

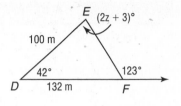

9. What is the measure of $\angle E$? (Lesson 4-2)

   A 18   C 43

   B 40   D 81

9. Ⓐ Ⓑ Ⓒ Ⓓ

10. Which of the following could not be $\overline{EF}$?
    (Lesson 5-4)

    F 20 m   G 53 m   H 75 m   J 80 m

10. Ⓕ Ⓖ Ⓗ Ⓙ

11. Which of the following inequalities is true? (Lesson 5-2)

    A $z \le 60$ B $z < 60$ C $z \ge 60$ D $z > 60$

11. Ⓐ Ⓑ Ⓒ Ⓓ

For Questions 12 and 13 refer to the figure.

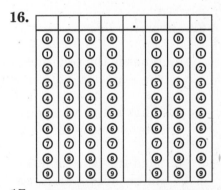

12. Which line segment is the shortest? (Lesson 5-2)

    F $\overline{PQ}$ G $\overline{QR}$

    H $\overline{RS}$ J $\overline{PS}$

12. Ⓕ Ⓖ Ⓗ Ⓙ

13. Which line segment is the longest? (Lesson 5-2)

    A $\overline{PQ}$ B $\overline{QR}$ C $\overline{RS}$ D $\overline{PS}$

13. Ⓐ Ⓑ Ⓒ Ⓓ

14. What is the perimeter of $\triangle MOP$ with vertices $M(0, 4)$, $O(0, 0)$, $P(3, 0)$? (Lesson 3-6)

    F −12   G −5   H 5   J 12

14. Ⓕ Ⓖ Ⓗ Ⓙ

15. Which of the following sets of numbers cannot be lengths of the sides of a triangle? (Lesson 5-4)

    A 1,2,3   B 2,3,4   C 3,4,5   D 4,5,6

15. Ⓐ Ⓑ Ⓒ Ⓓ

16.

				.			
⓪	⓪	⓪	⓪		⓪	⓪	⓪
①	①	①	①		①	①	①
②	②	②	②		②	②	②
③	③	③	③		③	③	③
④	④	④	④		④	④	④
⑤	⑤	⑤	⑤		⑤	⑤	⑤
⑥	⑥	⑥	⑥		⑥	⑥	⑥
⑦	⑦	⑦	⑦		⑦	⑦	⑦
⑧	⑧	⑧	⑧		⑧	⑧	⑧
⑨	⑨	⑨	⑨		⑨	⑨	⑨

Part 2: Griddable

Instructions: Enter your answer by writing each digit of the answer in a column box and then shading in the appropriate circle that corresponds to that entry.

16. If $\overline{BD}$ is an altitude of $\triangle ABC$, find x. (Lesson 5-2)

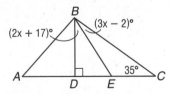

17.

				.			
⓪	⓪	⓪	⓪		⓪	⓪	⓪
①	①	①	①		①	①	①
②	②	②	②		②	②	②
③	③	③	③		③	③	③
④	④	④	④		④	④	④
⑤	⑤	⑤	⑤		⑤	⑤	⑤
⑥	⑥	⑥	⑥		⑥	⑥	⑥
⑦	⑦	⑦	⑦		⑦	⑦	⑦
⑧	⑧	⑧	⑧		⑧	⑧	⑧
⑨	⑨	⑨	⑨		⑨	⑨	⑨

17. The measures of two sides of $\triangle ABC$ are 19 and 15. The range for measure of the third side, n, would be $4 < n < $ _____? (Lesson 5-4)

5 Standardized Test Practice (continued)

Part 3: Short Response
Instructions: Write your answer in the space provided.

18. Find a counterexample for the statement *Five is the only whole number between 4.5 and 6.1.* (Lesson 2-1)

18._____

19. What is the length of the side opposite the vertex angle of isosceles $\triangle XYZ$ with vertices at $X(-3, 4)$, $Y(8, 6)$, and $Z(3, -4)$? (Lesson 4-1)

19._____

20. What is the distance between $A(-12, 12)$ and $B(-5, -12)$? (Lesson 3-6)

20._____

21. The vertices of $\triangle ABC$ are $A(-2, 3)$, $B(4, 3)$, and $C(-2, -3)$. Find the coordinates of each point of concurrency of $\triangle ABC$.

a. circumcenter

21a._____

b. centroid

21b._____

c. orthocenter

21c._____

22. Given the line $y = 5x + 2$:

a. What is the equation of the parallel line that intercepts the y-axis at -2? (Lesson 3-5)

22a._____

b. What is the equation of the perpendicular line that intersects $y = 5x + 2$ at $x = 0$? (Lesson 3-6)

22b._____

c. Find the point of intersection of the lines found in part a. and b. above? (Lesson 3-6)

22c._____

Answers (Anticipation Guide and Lesson 5–1)

Lesson Reading Guide — 5-1

Bisectors, Medians, and Altitudes

Get Ready for the Lesson

Read the introduction to Lesson 5-1 in your textbook.

Draw any triangle and connect each vertex to the midpoint of the opposite side to form the three medians of the triangle. Is the point where the three medians intersect the midpoint of each of the medians? **Sample answer: No; the intersection point appears to be more than halfway from each vertex to the midpoint of the opposite side.**

Read the Lesson

1. Underline the correct word or phrase to complete each sentence.
   a. Three or more lines that intersect at a common point are called (parallel/perpendicular/<u>concurrent</u>) lines.
   b. Any point on the perpendicular bisector of a segment is (parallel to/congruent to/<u>equidistant from</u>) the endpoints of the segment.
   c. A(n) (<u>altitude</u>/angle bisector/median/perpendicular bisector) of a triangle is a segment drawn from a vertex of the triangle perpendicular to the line containing the opposite side.
   d. The point of concurrency of the three perpendicular bisectors of a triangle is called the (orthocenter/<u>circumcenter</u>/centroid/incenter).
   e. Any point in the interior of an angle that is equidistant from the sides of that angle lies on the (median/<u>angle bisector</u>/altitude).
   f. The point of concurrency of the three angle bisectors of a triangle is called the (orthocenter/circumcenter/centroid/<u>incenter</u>).

2. In the figure, E is the midpoint of $\overline{AB}$, F is the midpoint of $\overline{BC}$, and G is the midpoint of $\overline{AC}$.
   a. Name the altitudes of $\triangle ABC$. **$\overline{AC}$, $\overline{BC}$, $\overline{CD}$**
   b. Name the medians of $\triangle ABC$. **$\overline{AF}$, $\overline{BG}$, $\overline{CE}$**
   c. Name the centroid of $\triangle ABC$. **H**
   d. Name the orthocenter of $\triangle ABC$. **C**
   e. If $AF = 12$ and $CE = 9$, find AH and HE. **$AH = 8$, $HE = 3$**

Remember What You Learned

3. A good way to remember something is to explain it to someone else. Suppose that a classmate is having trouble remembering whether the center of gravity of a triangle is the orthocenter, the centroid, the incenter, or the circumcenter which point it is. **Sample answer: The terms *centroid* and *center of gravity* mean the same thing and in both terms, the letters "cent" come at the beginning of the terms.**

Chapter 5   5   Glencoe Geometry

Anticipation Guide — 5

Relationships in Triangles

STEP 1 Before you begin Chapter 5
- Read each statement.
- Decide whether you Agree (A) or Disagree (D) with the statement.
- Write A or D in the first column OR if you are not sure whether you agree or disagree, write NS (Not Sure).

STEP 1 A, D, or NS	Statement	STEP 2 A or D
	1. Any point that is on the perpendicular bisector of a segment is equidistant from the endpoints of that segment.	A
	2. The circumcenter of a triangle is equidistant from the midpoints of each side of the triangle.	D
	3. Three or more parallel lines are called concurrent lines.	D
	4. Three altitudes can be drawn for any one triangle.	A
	5. A median of a triangle is any segment that contains the midpoint of a side of the triangle.	D
	6. The measure of an exterior angle of a triangle is always greater than the measures of either of its corresponding remote interior angles.	A
	7. The longest side in a triangle is opposite the smallest angle in that triangle.	D
	8. To write an indirect proof that two lines are perpendicular, begin by assuming the two lines are not perpendicular.	A
	9. The length of the longest side of a triangle is always greater than the sum of the lengths of the other two sides.	D
	10. In two triangles, if two pairs of sides are congruent, then the measure of the included angles determines which triangle has the longer third side.	A

STEP 2 After you complete Chapter 5
- Reread each statement and complete the last column by entering an A or a D.
- Did any of your opinions about the statements change from the first column?
- For those statements that you mark with a D, use a piece of paper to write an example of why you disagree.

Chapter 5   3   Glencoe Geometry

Copyright © Glencoe/McGraw-Hill, a division of The McGraw-Hill Companies, Inc.

5-1 Study Guide and Intervention (continued)

Bisectors, Medians, and Altitudes

Medians and Altitudes A **median** is a line segment that connects the vertex of a triangle to the midpoint of the opposite side. The three medians of a triangle intersect at the **centroid** of the triangle.

Centroid Theorem	The centroid of a triangle is located two thirds of the distance from a vertex to the midpoint of the side opposite the vertex on a median.

$AL = \frac{2}{3}AE, BL = \frac{2}{3}BF, CL = \frac{2}{3}CD$

Example Points *R*, *S*, and *T* are the midpoints of $\overline{AB}$, $\overline{BC}$ and $\overline{AC}$, respectively. Find *x*, *y*, and *z*.

$CU = \frac{2}{3}CR$ $\qquad BU = \frac{2}{3}BT$ $\qquad AU = \frac{2}{3}AS$

$6x = \frac{2}{3}(6x + 15)$ $\quad 24 = \frac{2}{3}(24 + 3y - 3)$ $\quad 6z + 4 = \frac{2}{3}(6z + 4 + 11)$

$9x = 6x + 15$ $\qquad 36 = 24 + 3y - 3$ $\qquad \frac{3}{2}(6z + 4) = 6z + 4 + 11$

$3x = 15$ $\qquad\qquad 36 = 21 + 3y$ $\qquad 9z + 6 = 6z + 15$

$x = 5$ $\qquad\qquad\quad 15 = 3y$ $\qquad\qquad 3z = 9$

$\qquad\qquad\qquad\qquad 5 = y$ $\qquad\qquad\qquad z = 3$

Exercises

Find the value of each variable.

1.

$x = 4$

$\overline{BD}$ is a median.

2.

$x = 6; y = 5$

$AB = CB; D, E,$ and F are midpoints.

3. $x = 3; y = 5$

4. **M, O, P are midpoints.** $x = 12; y = 5; z = 2$

5. $x = 2; y = 2; z = 2$

D is the centroid of $\triangle ABC$.

6. $x = 6; y = 5; z = 8$

V is the centroid of $\triangle RST$;
$TP = 18; MS = 15; RN = 24$

7. For what kind of triangle are the medians and angle bisectors the same segments? **equilateral triangle**

8. For what kind of triangle is the centroid outside the triangle? **not possible**

Chapter 5   7   *Glencoe Geometry*

5-1 Study Guide and Intervention

Bisectors, Medians, and Altitudes

Perpendicular Bisectors and Angle Bisectors A **perpendicular bisector** of a side of a triangle is a line, segment, or ray in the same plane as the triangle that is perpendicular to the side and passes through its midpoint. Another special segment, ray, or line is an **angle bisector**, which divides an angle into two congruent angles.

Two properties of perpendicular bisectors are:
(1) a point is on the perpendicular bisector of a segment if and only if it is equidistant from the endpoints of the segment, and
(2) the three perpendicular bisectors of the sides of a triangle meet at a point, called the **circumcenter** of the triangle, that is equidistant from the three vertices of the triangle.

Two properties of angle bisectors are:
(1) a point is on the angle bisector of an angle if and only if it is equidistant from the sides of the angle, and
(2) the three angle bisectors of a triangle meet at a point, called the **incenter** of the triangle, that is equidistant from the three sides of the triangle.

Example 1 $\overline{BD}$ is the perpendicular bisector of $\overline{AC}$. Find *x*.

$\overline{BD}$ is the perpendicular bisector of $\overline{AC}$, so $AD = DC$.

$3x + 8 = 5x - 6$
$14 = 2x$
$7 = x$

Example 2 $\overline{MR}$ is the angle bisector of $\angle NMP$. Find *x* if $m\angle 1 = 5x + 8$ and $m\angle 2 = 8x - 16$.

$\overline{MR}$ is the angle bisector of $\angle NMP$, so $m\angle 1 = m\angle 2$.

$5x + 8 = 8x - 16$
$24 = 3x$
$8 = x$

Exercises

Find the value of each variable.

1.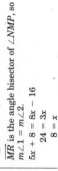

$\overline{DE}$ is the perpendicular bisector of $\overline{AC}$.
$x = 7$

2.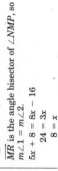

$\triangle CDF$ is equilateral.
$x = 10; y = 2$

3.

$\overline{DF}$ bisects $\angle CDE$.
$x = 7.5$

4. For what kinds of triangle(s) can the perpendicular bisector of a side also be an angle bisector of the angle opposite the side? **isosceles triangle, equilateral triangle**

5. For what kind of triangle do the perpendicular bisectors intersect in a point outside the triangle? **obtuse triangle**

Chapter 5   6   *Glencoe Geometry*

Left Page

NAME _____ DATE _____ PERIOD _____

5-1 Skills Practice
Bisectors, Medians, and Altitudes

ALGEBRA For Exercises 1–4, use the given information to find each value.

1. Find x if $\overline{EG}$ is a median of $\triangle DEF$.

$x = 9$

2. Find x and RT if $\overline{SU}$ is a median of $\triangle RST$.

$x = 18;\ RT = 120$

3. Find x and EF if $\overline{BD}$ is an angle bisector.

$x = 3.5;\ EF = 13$

4. Find x and IJ if $\overline{HK}$ is an altitude of $\triangle HIJ$.

$x = 29;\ IJ = 57$

ALGEBRA For Exercises 5–7, use the following information.
In $\triangle LMN$, P, Q, and R are the midpoints of $\overline{LM}$, $\overline{MN}$, and $\overline{LN}$, respectively.

5. Find x. 4
6. Find y. 0.8
7. Find z. 0.7

ALGEBRA Lines a, b, and c are perpendicular bisectors of $\triangle PQR$ and meet at A.

8. Find x. 1
9. Find y. 6
10. Find z. 2

COORDINATE GEOMETRY The vertices of $\triangle HIJ$ are $J(1, 0)$, $H(6, 0)$, and $I(3, 6)$. Find the coordinates of the points of concurrency of $\triangle HIJ$.

11. orthocenter
$(3, 1)$

12. centroid
$\left(\dfrac{10}{3}, 2\right)$

13. circumcenter
$\left(\dfrac{7}{2}, \dfrac{5}{2}\right)$

Right Page

NAME _____ DATE _____ PERIOD _____

5-1 Practice
Bisectors, Medians, and Altitudes

ALGEBRA In $\triangle ABC$, $\overline{BF}$ is the angle bisector of $\angle ABC$, $\overline{AE}$, $\overline{BF}$, and $\overline{CD}$ are medians, and P is the centroid.

1. Find x if $DP = 4x - 3$ and $CP = 30$. 4.5
2. Find y if $AP = y$ and $EP = 18$. 36
3. Find z if $FP = 5z + 10$ and $BP = 42$. 2.2
4. If $m\angle ABC = x$ and $m\angle BAC = m\angle BCA = 2x - 10$, is $\overline{BF}$ an altitude? Explain.
Yes; since $x = 40$ and $\overline{BF}$ is an angle bisector, it follows that $m\angle BAF = 70$ and $m\angle ABF = 20$. So $m\angle AFB = 90$, and $\overline{BF} \perp \overline{AC}$.

ALGEBRA In $\triangle PRS$, $\overline{PT}$ is an altitude and $\overline{PX}$ is a median.

5. Find RS if $RX = x + 7$ and $SX = 3x - 11$.
32
6. Find RT if $RT = x - 6$ and $m\angle PTR = 8x - 6$.
6

ALGEBRA In $\triangle DEF$, $\overline{GI}$ is a perpendicular bisector.

7. Find x if $EH = 16$ and $FH = 6x - 5$.
3.5
8. Find y if $EG = 3.2y - 1$ and $FG = 2y + 5$.
5
9. Find z if $m\angle EGH = 12z$.
7.5

COORDINATE GEOMETRY The vertices of $\triangle STU$ are $S(0, 1)$, $T(4, 7)$, and $U(8, -3)$. Find the coordinates of the points of concurrency of $\triangle STU$.

10. orthocenter
$\left(\dfrac{5}{4}, \dfrac{3}{2}\right)$

11. centroid
$\left(4, \dfrac{5}{3}\right)$

12. circumcenter
$\left(\dfrac{43}{8}, \dfrac{7}{4}\right)$ or $(5.375, 1.75)$

13. **MOBILES** Nabuko wants to construct a mobile out of flat triangles so that the surfaces of the triangles hang parallel to the floor when the mobile is suspended. How can Nabuko be certain that she hangs the triangles to achieve this effect? She needs to hang each triangle from its center of gravity or centroid, which is the point at which the three medians of the triangle intersect.

Left page

5-1 Word Problem Practice

Bisectors, Medians, and Altitudes

1. BALANCING Johanna balanced a triangle flat on her finger tip. What point of the triangle must Johanna be touching?

centroid

2. PICNICS Marsha and Bill are going to the park for a picnic. The park is triangular. One side of the park is bordered by a river and the other two sides are bordered by busy streets. Marsha and Bill want to find a spot that is equally far away from the river and the streets. At what point in the park should they set up their picnic?

at the incenter of the park

3. MOVING Martin has 3 grown children. The figure shows the locations of Martin's children on a map that has a coordinate plane on it. Martin would like to move to a location that is the same distance from all three of his children. What are the coordinates of the location on the map that is equidistant from all three children?

$(0, -2)$

4. NEIGHBORHOOD Amanda is looking at her neighborhood map. She notices that her house along with the homes of her friends Brian, and Cathy can be the vertices of a triangle. The map is on a coordinate grid. Amanda's house is at the point $(1, 3)$ Brian's is at $(5, -1)$, and Cathy's is at $(4, 5)$. Where would the three friends meet if they each left their houses at the same time and walked to the opposite side of the triangle along the path of shortest distance from their house?

$\left(\dfrac{11}{5}, \dfrac{16}{5}\right)$

PLAZAS For Exercises 5–7, use the following information.

An architect is designing a triangular plaza. For aesthetic purposes, the architect pays special attention to the location of the centroid C and the circumcenter O.

5. Give an example of a triangular plaza where $C = O$. If no such example exists, state that this is *impossible*.

an equilateral triangle

6. Give an example of a triangular plaza where C is inside the plaza and O is outside the plaza. If no such example exists, state that this is *impossible*.

an obtuse triangle

7. Give an example of a triangular plaza where C is outside the plaza and O is inside the plaza. If no such example exists, state that this is *impossible*.

impossible

Right page

5-1 Enrichment

Inscribed and Circumscribed Circles

The three angle bisectors of a triangle intersect in a single point called the **incenter**. This point is the center of a circle that just touches the three sides of the triangle. Except for the three points where the circle touches the sides, the circle is inside the triangle. The circle is said to be inscribed in the triangle.

1. With a compass and a straightedge, construct the inscribed circle for $\triangle PQR$ by following the steps below.

Step 1 Construct the bisectors of $\angle R$ and $\angle Q$. Label the point where the bisectors meet A.

Step 2 Construct a perpendicular segment from A to $\overline{RQ}$. Use the letter B to label the point where the perpendicular segment intersects $\overline{RQ}$.

Step 3 Use a compass to draw the circle with center at A and radius $\overline{AB}$.

Construct the inscribed circle in each triangle.

2.

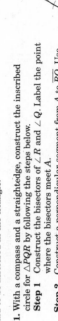

3.

The three perpendicular bisectors of the sides of a triangle also meet in a single point. This point is the center of the circumscribed circle, which passes through each vertex of the triangle. Except for the three points where the circle touches the triangle, the circle is outside the triangle.

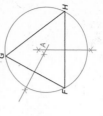

4. Follow the steps below to construct the circumscribed circle for $\triangle FGH$.

Step 1 Construct the perpendicular bisectors of $\overline{FG}$ and $\overline{FH}$. Use the letter A to label the point where the perpendicular bisectors meet.

Step 2 Draw the circle that has center A and radius $\overline{AF}$.

Construct the circumscribed circle for each triangle.

5.

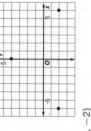

6.

NAME _____ DATE _____ PERIOD _____

5-2 Study Guide and Intervention
Inequalities and Triangles

Angle Inequalities Properties of inequalities, including the Transitive, Addition, Subtraction, Multiplication, and Division Properties of Inequality, can be used with measures of angles and segments. There is also a Comparison Property of Inequality.

For any real numbers a and b, either $a < b$, $a = b$, or $a > b$.

The Exterior Angle Theorem can be used to prove this inequality involving an exterior angle.

Exterior Angle Inequality Theorem	If an angle is an exterior angle of a triangle, then its measure is greater than the measure of either of its corresponding remote interior angles.

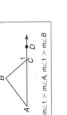

$m\angle 1 > m\angle A, m\angle 1 > m\angle B$

Example List all angles of $\triangle EFG$ whose measures are less than $m\angle 1$.
The measure of an exterior angle is greater than the measure of either remote interior angle. So $m\angle 3 < m\angle 1$ and $m\angle 4 < m\angle 1$.

Exercises

List all angles that satisfy the stated condition.

1. all angles whose measures are less than $m\angle 1$ $\angle 3, \angle 4$

2. all angles whose measures are greater than $m\angle 3$ $\angle 1, \angle 5$

3. all angles whose measures are less than $m\angle 1$ $\angle 5, \angle 6$

4. all angles whose measures are greater than $m\angle 1$ $\angle 7$

5. all angles whose measures are less than $m\angle 7$ $\angle 1, \angle 3, \angle 5, \angle 6, \angle TUV$

6. all angles whose measures are greater than $m\angle 2$ $\angle 4$

7. all angles whose measures are greater than $m\angle 5$ $\angle 1, \angle 7, \angle TUV$

8. all angles whose measures are less than $m\angle 4$ $\angle 2, \angle 3$

9. all angles whose measures are less than $m\angle 1$
$\angle 4, \angle 5, \angle 7, \angle NPR$

10. all angles whose measures are greater than $m\angle 4$
$\angle 1, \angle 8, \angle OPN, \angle ROQ$

Exercises 1–2

Exercises 3–8

Exercises 9–10

NAME _____ DATE _____ PERIOD _____

5-2 Lesson Reading Guide
Inequalities and Triangles

Get Ready for the Lesson

Read the introduction to Lesson 5-2 in your textbook.

• Which side of the patio is opposite the largest corner? **the 51-foot side**

• Which side of the patio is opposite the smallest corner? **the 45-foot side**

Read the Lesson

1. Name the property of inequality that is illustrated by each of the following.
a. If $x > 8$ and $8 > y$, then $x > y$. **Transitive Property**
b. If $x < y$, then $x - 7.5 < y - 7.5$. **Subtraction Property**
c. If $x > y$, then $-3x < -3y$. **Multiplication Property**
d. If x is any real number, $x > 0$, $x = 0$, or $x < 0$. **Comparison Property**

2. Use the definition of inequality to write an *equation* that shows that each inequality is true.
a. $20 > 12$ $20 = 12 + 8$
b. $101 > 99$ $101 = 99 + 2$
c. $8 > -2$ $8 = -2 + 10$
d. $7 > -7$ $7 = -7 + 14$
e. $-11 > -12$ $-11 = -12 + 1$
f. $-30 > -45$ $-30 = -45 + 15$

3. In the figure, $m\angle IJK = 45$ and $m\angle H > m\angle I$.

a. Arrange the following angles in order from largest to smallest: $\angle I, \angle IJK, \angle H, \angle IJH$ $\angle IJH, \angle IJK, \angle H, \angle I$
b. Arrange the sides of $\triangle HIJ$ in order from shortest to longest.
$\overline{HJ}, \overline{IJ}, \overline{HI}$
c. Is $\triangle HIJ$ an acute, right, or obtuse triangle? Explain your reasoning.
Obtuse; sample answer: $\angle IJH$ **is obtuse because** $m\angle IJH = 180 - m\angle IJK = 135$. **Therefore,** $\triangle HIJ$ **is obtuse because it has an obtuse angle.**
d. Is $\triangle HIJ$ scalene, isosceles, or equilateral? Explain your reasoning.
Scalene; sample answer: the three angles of $\triangle HIJ$ **all have different measures, so the sides opposite them must have different lengths.**

Remember What You Learned

4. A good way to remember a new geometric theorem is to relate it to a theorem you learned earlier. Explain how the Exterior Angle Inequality Theorem is related to the Exterior Angle Theorem, and why the Exterior Angle Inequality Theorem must be true if the Exterior Angle Theorem is true.
Sample answer: The Exterior Angle Theorem says that the measure of an exterior angle of a triangle is equal to the sum of the measures of the two remote interior angles, while the Exterior Angle Inequality Theorem says that the measure of an exterior angle is greater than the measure of either remote interior angle. If a number is equal to the sum of two positive numbers, it must be greater than each of those two numbers.

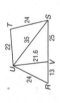

NAME _____ DATE _____ PERIOD _____

5-2 Skills Practice

Inequalities and Triangles

Determine which angle has the greatest measure.

1. ∠1, ∠3, ∠4   ∠1

2. ∠4, ∠5, ∠7   ∠4

3. ∠2, ∠3, ∠6   ∠6

4. ∠5, ∠6, ∠8   ∠8

Use the Exterior Angle Inequality Theorem to list all angles that satisfy the stated condition.

5. all angles whose measures are less than $m\angle 1$
∠2, ∠3, ∠4, ∠5, ∠7, ∠8

6. all angles whose measures are less than $m\angle 9$
∠2, ∠4, ∠6, ∠7

7. all angles whose measures are greater than $m\angle 5$
∠1, ∠3

8. all angles whose measures are greater than $m\angle 8$
∠1, ∠3, ∠5

Determine the relationship between the measures of the given angles.

9. $m\angle ABD, m\angle BAD$ $m\angle ABD > m\angle BAD$

10. $m\angle ADB, m\angle BAD$ $m\angle ADB < m\angle BAD$

11. $m\angle BCD, m\angle CDB$ $m\angle BCD > m\angle CDB$

12. $m\angle CBD, m\angle CDB$ $m\angle CBD > m\angle CDB$

Determine the relationship between the lengths of the given sides.

13. $\overline{LM}, \overline{LP}$ $LM < LP$

14. $\overline{MP}, \overline{MN}$ $MP > MN$

15. $\overline{MN}, \overline{NP}$ $MN < NP$

16. $\overline{MP}, \overline{LP}$ $MP < LP$

Chapter 5   15   *Glencoe Geometry*

NAME _____ DATE _____ PERIOD _____

5-2 Study Guide and Intervention *(continued)*

Inequalities and Triangles

Angle-Side Relationships When the sides of triangles are not congruent, there is a relationship between the sides and angles of the triangles.

- If one side of a triangle is longer than another side, then the angle opposite the longer side has a greater measure than the angle opposite the shorter side.
- If one angle of a triangle has a greater measure than another angle, then the side opposite the greater angle is longer than the side opposite the lesser angle.

If $AC > AB$, then $m\angle B > m\angle C$.
If $m\angle A > m\angle C$, then $BC > AB$.

Example 1 List the angles in order from least to greatest measure.
∠T, ∠R, ∠S

Example 2 List the sides in order from shortest to longest.
$\overline{CB}, \overline{AB}, \overline{AC}$

Exercises

List the angles or sides in order from least to greatest measure.

1. ∠T, ∠R, ∠S

2. $\overline{RS}, \overline{ST}, \overline{RT}$

3. ∠C, ∠B, ∠A

Determine the relationship between the measures of the given angles.

4. ∠R, ∠RUS $m\angle R < m\angle RUS$

5. ∠T, ∠UST $m\angle T > m\angle UST$

6. ∠UVS, ∠R $m\angle UVS > m\angle R$

Determine the relationship between the lengths of the given sides.

7. $\overline{AC}, \overline{BC}$ $AC > BC$

8. $\overline{BC}, \overline{DB}$ $BC > DB$

9. $\overline{AC}, \overline{DB}$ $AC > DB$

Chapter 5   14   *Glencoe Geometry*

Left page

NAME _____ DATE _____ PERIOD _____

5-2 Practice

Inequalities and Triangles

Determine which angle has the greatest measure.

1. ∠1, ∠3, ∠4

   ∠4

2. ∠4, ∠8, ∠9

   ∠4

3. ∠2, ∠3, ∠7

   ∠7

4. ∠7, ∠8, ∠10

   ∠10

Use the Exterior Angle Inequality Theorem to list all angles that satisfy the stated condition.

5. all angles whose measures are less than m∠1

   ∠3, ∠4, ∠5, ∠7, ∠8

6. all angles whose measures are less than m∠3

   ∠5, ∠7, ∠8

7. all angles whose measures are greater than m∠7

   ∠1, ∠3, ∠5, ∠9

8. all angles whose measures are greater than m∠2

   ∠6, ∠9

Determine the relationship between the measures of the given angles.

9. m∠QRW, m∠RWQ

   m∠QRW < ∠RWQ

10. m∠RTW, m∠TWR

    m∠RTW < ∠TWR

11. m∠RST, m∠TRS

    m∠RST > ∠TRS

12. m∠WQR, m∠QRW

    m∠WQR < ∠QRW

Determine the relationship between the lengths of the given sides.

13. $\overline{DH}, \overline{GH}$

    DH > GH

14. $\overline{DE}, \overline{DG}$

    DE < DG

15. $\overline{EG}, \overline{FG}$

    EG < FG

16. $\overline{DE}, \overline{EG}$

    DE > EG

17. **SPORTS** The figure shows the position of three trees on one part of a Frisbee™ course. At which tree position is the angle between the trees the greatest? **2**

Right page

NAME _____ DATE _____ PERIOD _____

5-2 Word Problem Practice

Inequalities and Triangles

1. **DISTANCE** Carl and Rose live on the same straight road. From their balconies they can see a flagpole in the distance. The angle that each person's line of sight to the flagpole makes with the road is the same. How do their distances from the flagpole compare?

   They are equal.

2. **OBTUSE TRIANGLES** Don notices that the side opposite the right angle in a right triangle is always the longest of the three sides. Is this also true of the side opposite the obtuse angle in an obtuse triangle? Explain.

   Yes. Since an obtuse triangle only has 1 obtuse angle and 2 acute angles, the side opposite the obtuse angle is the longest side.

3. **STRING** Jake built a triangular structure with three black sticks. He tied one end of a string to vertex M and the other end to a point on the stick opposite M, pulling the string taut. Prove that the length of the string cannot exceed the longer of the two sides of the structure.

   Sample answer: The string divides the triangle in two; one of these triangles is right or obtuse because one side of the string must make a right or obtuse angle with the stick. In this triangle, the side opposite the right or obtuse angle is longer than the string and that side is also a side of the triangle.

4. **SQUARES** Matthew has three different squares. He arranges the squares to form a triangle as shown. Based on the information, list the squares in order from the one with the smallest perimeter to the one with the largest perimeter.

   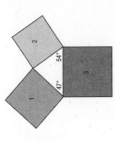

   2, 1, 3

CITIES For Exercises 5 and 6, use the following information.

Stella is going to Texas to visit a friend. As she was looking at a map to see where she might want to go, she noticed the cities Austin, Dallas, and Abilene formed a triangle. She wanted to determine how the distances between the cities were related, so she used a protractor to measure two angles.

5. Based on the information in the figure, which of the two cities are nearest to each other?

   Dallas and Abilene

6. Based on the information in the figure, which of the two cities are farthest apart from each other?

   Abilene and Austin

5-2 Graphing Calculator Activity

Cabri Junior: Inequalities and Triangles

Cabri Junior can be used to investigate the relationships between angles and sides of a triangle.

Step 1 Use Cabri Jr. to draw and label a triangle.
- Select **F2 Triangle** to draw a triangle.
- Move the cursor to where you want the first vertex. Press **ENTER**.
- Repeat this procedure to determine the next two vertices of the triangle.
- Select **F5 Alph-num** to label each vertex.
- Move the cursor to a vertex, press **ENTER**, enter A, and press **ENTER** again.
- Repeat this procedure to label vertex B and vertex C.

Step 2 Draw an exterior angle of △ABC.
- Select **F2 Line** to draw a line through $\overline{BC}$.
- Select **F2 Point, Point on** to draw a point on $\overline{BC}$ so that C is between B and the new point.
- Select **F5 Alph-num** to label the point D.

Step 3 Find the measures of the three interior angles and the exterior angle, ∠ACD.
- Select **F5 Measure, Angle.**
- To find the measure of ∠ABC, select points A, B, and C (with the vertex B as the second point selected).
- Repeat to find the remaining angle measures.

Step 4 Find the measure of each side of △ABC.
- Select **F5 Measure, D. & Length.**
- To find the length of $\overline{AB}$, select point A and then select point B.
- Repeat this procedure to find the lengths of $\overline{BC}$ and $\overline{CA}$.

Exercises

Analyze your drawing.

1. What is the relationship between $m\angle ACD$ and $m\angle ABC$? $m\angle ACD$ and $m\angle BAC$?
   Sample answer: $m\angle ACD > m\angle ABC$; $m\angle ACD > m\angle BAC$

2. Make a conjecture about the relationship between the measures of an exterior angle (∠ACD) and its two remote interior angles (∠ABC and ∠BAC). **The measure of an exterior angle is equal to the sum of the measure of the two remote interior angles.**

3. Change the dimensions of the triangle by moving point A. (Press **CLEAR** so the pointer becomes a black arrow. Move the pointer close to point A until the arrow becomes transparent and point A is blinking. Press **ALPHA** to change the arrow to a hand. Then move the point.) Is your conjecture still true? **yes**

4. Which side of the triangle is the longest? the shortest? **See students' work.**

5. Which angle measure (not including the exterior angle) is the greatest? the least?
   See students' work.

6. Make a conjecture about where the longest side is in relationship to the greatest angle and where the shortest side is in relationship to the least angle.
   The longest side is opposite the greatest angle. The shortest side is opposite the least angle.

5-2 Enrichment

Construction Problem

The diagram below shows segment AB adjacent to a closed region. The problem requires that you construct another segment XY to the right of the closed region such that points A, B, X, and Y are collinear. You are not allowed to touch or cross the closed region with your compass or straightedge.

Follow these instructions to construct a segment XY so that it is collinear with segment AB.

1. Construct the perpendicular bisector of $\overline{AB}$. Label the midpoint as point C, and the line as m.

2. Mark two points P and Q on line m that lie well above the closed region. Construct the perpendicular bisector n of $\overline{PQ}$. Label the intersection of lines m and n as point D.

3. Mark points R and S on line n that lie well to the right of the closed region. Construct the perpendicular bisector $\mathcal{k}$ of $\overline{RS}$. Label the intersection of lines n and $\mathcal{k}$ as point E.

4. Mark point X on line $\mathcal{k}$ so that X is below line n and so that $\overline{EX}$ is congruent to $\overline{DC}$.

5. Mark points T and V on line $\mathcal{k}$ on opposite sides of X, so that $\overline{XT}$ and $\overline{XV}$ are congruent. Construct the perpendicular bisector ℓ of $\overline{TV}$. Call the point where the line ℓ hits the boundary of the closed region point Y. $\overline{XY}$ corresponds to the new road.

5-2 Geometer's Sketchpad Activity

Inequalities and Triangles

The Geometer's Sketchpad can be used to investigate the relationships between angles and sides of a triangle.

Step 1 Use The Geometer's Sketchpad to draw a triangle and one exterior angle.

- Construct a ray by selecting the Ray tool from the toolbar. First, click where you want the first point. Then click a second point to draw the ray.
- Next, select the Segment tool from the toolbar. Use the endpoint of the ray as the first point for the segment and click on a second point to construct the segment.
- Construct another segment joining the second point of the previous segment to a point on the ray.
- Display the labels for each point. Use the Selection Arrow tool to select all four points. Display the labels by selecting **Show Label** from the **Display** menu.

$m\angle ABC = 69.29°$
$m\angle BCA = 55.92°$
$m\angle BAC = 54.78°$
$m\angle BCD = 124.08°$
$AB = 2.20$ cm
$BC = 2.17$ cm
$AC = 2.49$ cm

Step 2 Find the measures of each angle.

- To find the measure of angle ABC, use the Selection Arrow tool to select points A, B, and C (with the vertex B as the second point selected). Then, under the **Measure** menu, select **Angle.** Use this method to find the remaining angle measures, including the exterior angle, $\angle BCD$.

Step 3 Find the measures of each side of the triangle.

- To find the measure of side AB, select A and then B. Next, under the **Measure** menu, select **Distance.** Use this method to find the other two sides.

Exercises

Analyze your drawing.

1. What is the relationship between $m\angle BCD$ and $m\angle ABC$ and $m\angle ABC$? $m\angle BCD$ and $m\angle BAC$?
   Sample answer: $m\angle BCD > m\angle ABC$; $m\angle BCD > m\angle BAC$

2. Make a conjecture about the relationship between the measures of an exterior angle ($\angle BCD$) and its two remote interior angles ($\angle ABC$ and $\angle BAC$). The measure of an exterior angle is equal to the sum of the measure of the two remote interior angles.

3. Change the dimensions of the triangle by selecting point A with the pointer tool and moving it. Is your conjecture still true? yes

4. Which side of the triangle is the longest? the shortest? See students' work.

5. Which angle measure (not including the exterior angle) is the greatest? the least? See students' work.

6. Make a conjecture about where the longest side is in relationship to the greatest angle and where the shortest side is in relationship to the least angle.
   The longest side is opposite the greatest angle. The shortest side is opposite the least angle.

5-3 Lesson Reading Guide

Indirect Proof

Get Ready for the Lesson

Read the introduction to Lesson 5-3 in your textbook.

How could the author of a murder mystery use indirect reasoning to show that a particular suspect is not guilty? **Sample answer: Assume that the person is guilty. Then show that this assumption contradicts evidence that has been gathered about the crime.**

Read the Lesson

1. Supply the missing words to complete the list of steps involved in writing an indirect proof.

   Step 1 Assume that the conclusion is _____false_____.

   Step 2 Show that this assumption leads to a __contradiction__ of the __hypothesis__ or some other fact, such as a definition, postulate, __theorem__, or corollary.

   Step 3 Point out that the assumption must be _____false_____ and, therefore, the conclusion must be _____true_____.

2. State the assumption that you would make to start an indirect proof of each statement.

   a. If $-6x > 30$, then $x < -5$. $x \geq -5$

   b. If n is a multiple of 6, then n is a multiple of 3. n is not a multiple of 3.

   c. If a and b are both odd, then ab is odd. ab is even.

   d. If a is positive and b is negative, then ab is negative. ab is greater than or equal to 0.

   e. If F is between E and D, then $EF + FD = ED$. $EF + FD \neq ED$

   f. In a plane, if two lines are perpendicular to the same line, then they are parallel.   Two lines are not parallel.

   g. Refer to the figure.
   If $AB = AC$, then $m\angle B = m\angle C$.
   $m\angle B \neq m\angle C$

   h. Refer to the figure.
   In $\triangle PQR$, $PR + QR > QP$.
   $PR + QR \leq QP$

Remember What You Learned

3. A good way to remember a new concept in mathematics is to relate it to something you have already learned. How is the process of indirect proof related to the relationship between a conditional statement and its contrapositive? **Sample answer: The contrapositive of the conditional statement $p \rightarrow q$ is the statement $\sim q \rightarrow \sim p$. In an indirect proof of a conditional statement $p \rightarrow q$, you assume that q is false and show that this implies that p is false, that is, you show that $\sim q \rightarrow \sim p$ is true. Because a statement is logically equivalent to its contrapositive, proving the contrapositive is true is a way of proving the original conditional is true.**

5-3 Study Guide and Intervention

NAME _____ DATE _____ PERIOD _____

Indirect Proof

Indirect Proof with Algebra One way to prove that a statement is true is to assume that its conclusion is false and then show that this assumption leads to a contradiction of the hypothesis, a definition, postulate, theorem, or other statement that is accepted as true. That contradiction means that the conclusion cannot be false, so the conclusion must be true. This is known as **indirect proof.**

Steps for Writing an Indirect Proof
1. Assume that the conclusion is false.
2. Show that this assumption leads to a contradiction.
3. Point out that the assumption must be false, and therefore, the conclusion must be true.

Example Given: $3x + 5 > 8$
Prove: $x > 1$

Step 1 Assume that x is not greater than 1. That is, $x = 1$ or $x < 1$.

Step 2 Make a table for several possibilities for $x = 1$ or $x < 1$. The contradiction is that when $x = 1$ or $x < 1$, then $3x + 5$ is not greater than 8.

x	$3x + 5$
1	8
0	5
-1	2
-2	-1
-3	-4

Step 3 This contradicts the given information that $3x + 5 > 8$. The assumption that x is not greater than 1 must be false, which means that the statement "$x > 1$" must be true.

Exercises

Write the assumption you would make to start an indirect proof of each statement.

1. If $2x > 14$, then $x > 7$. $x \leq 7$

2. For all real numbers, if $a + b > c$, then $a > c - b$. $a \leq c - b$

Complete the proof.
Given: n is an integer and n^2 is even.
Prove: n is even.

3. Assume that n is not even. That is, assume n is odd.

4. Then n can be expressed as $2a + 1$ by **the meaning of odd number.**

5. $n^2 = (2a + 1)^2$ — Substitution

6. $= (2a + 1)(2a + 1)$ — Multiply.

7. $= 4a^2 + 4a + 1$ — Simplify.

8. $= 2(2a^2 + 2a) + 1$ — **Distributive Property**

9. $2(2a^2 + 2a) + 1$ is an odd number. This contradicts the given that n^2 is even, so the assumption must be **false.**

10. Therefore, n is even.

5-3 Study Guide and Intervention (continued)

NAME _____ DATE _____ PERIOD _____

Indirect Proof

Indirect Proof with Geometry To write an indirect proof in geometry, you assume that the conclusion is false. Then you show that the assumption leads to a contradiction. The contradiction shows that the conclusion cannot be false, so it must be true.

Example Given: $m\angle C = 100$
Prove: $\angle A$ is not a right angle.

Step 1 Assume that $\angle A$ is a right angle.

Step 2 Show that this leads to a contradiction. If $\angle A$ is a right angle, then $m\angle A = 90$ and $m\angle C + m\angle A = 100 + 90 = 190$. Thus the sum of the measures of the angles of $\triangle ABC$ is greater than 180.

Step 3 The conclusion that the sum of the measures of the angles of $\triangle ABC$ is greater than 180 is a contradiction of a known property. The assumption that $\angle A$ is a right angle must be false, which means that the statement "$\angle A$ is not a right angle" must be true.

Exercises

Write the assumption you would make to start an indirect proof of each statement.

1. If $m\angle A = 90$, then $m\angle B = 45$.
$m\angle B \neq 45$

2. If $\overline{AV}$ is not congruent to $\overline{VE}$, then $\triangle AVE$ is not isosceles.
$\triangle AVE$ is isosceles.

Complete the proof.
Given: $\angle 1 \cong \angle 2$ and $\overline{DG}$ is not congruent to $\overline{FG}$.
Prove: $\overline{DE}$ is not congruent to $\overline{FE}$.

3. Assume that $\overline{DE} \cong \overline{FE}$. — Assume the conclusion is false.

4. $\overline{EG} \cong \overline{EG}$ — **Reflexive Property**

5. $\triangle EDG \cong \triangle EFG$ — **SAS**

6. $\overline{DG} \cong \overline{FG}$ — **CPCTC**

7. This contradicts the given information, so the assumption must be false.

8. Therefore, $\overline{DE}$ is not congruent to $\overline{FE}$.

NAME _____ DATE _____ PERIOD _____

5-3 Skills Practice
Indirect Proof

Write the assumption you would make to start an indirect proof of each statement.

1. $m\angle ABC < m\angle CBA$

$m\angle ABC \geq m\angle CBA$

2. $\triangle DEF \cong \triangle RST$

$\triangle DEF \ncong \triangle RST$

3. Line a is perpendicular to line b.

Line a is not perpendicular to line b.

4. $\angle 5$ is supplementary to $\angle 6$.

$\angle 5$ is not supplementary to $\angle 6$.

PROOF Write an indirect proof.

5. **Given:** $x^2 + 8 \leq 12$
Prove: $x \leq 2$
Proof:
Step 1: Assume $x > 2$.
Step 2: If $x > 2$, then $x^2 > 4$. But if $x^2 > 4$, it follows that $x^2 + 8 > 12$. This contradicts the given fact that $x^2 + 8 \leq 12$.
Step 3: Since the assumption of $x > 2$ leads to a contradiction, it must be false. Therefore, $x \leq 2$ must be true.

6. **Given:** $\angle D \ncong \angle F$.
Prove: $DE \neq EF$

Proof:
Step 1: Assume $DE = EF$.
Step 2: If $DE = EF$, then $\overline{DE} \cong \overline{EF}$ by the definition of congruent segments. But if $\overline{DE} \cong \overline{EF}$, then $\angle D \cong \angle F$ by the Isosceles Triangle Theorem. This contradicts the given information that $\angle D \ncong \angle F$.
Step 3: Since the assumption that $DE = EF$ leads to a contradiction, it must be false. Therefore, it must be true that $DE \neq EF$.

NAME _____ DATE _____ PERIOD _____

5-3 Practice
Indirect Proof

Write the assumption you would make to start an indirect proof of each statement.

1. $\overline{BD}$ bisects $\angle ABC$.

$\overline{BD}$ does not bisect $\angle ABC$.

2. $RT = TS$

$RT \neq TS$

PROOF Write an indirect proof.

3. **Given:** $-4x + 2 < -10$
Prove: $x > 3$
Proof:
Step 1: Assume $x \leq 3$.
Step 2: If $x \leq 3$, then $-4x \geq -12$. But $-4x \geq -12$ implies that $-4x + 2 \geq -10$, which contradicts the given inequality.
Step 3: Since the assumption that $x \leq 3$ leads to a contradiction, it must be true that $x > 3$.

4. **Given:** $m\angle 2 + m\angle 3 \neq 180$
Prove: $a \nparallel b$
Proof:
Step 1: Assume $a \parallel b$.
Step 2: If $a \parallel b$, then the consecutive interior angles $\angle 2$ and $\angle 3$ are supplementary. Thus $m\angle 2 + m\angle 3 = 180$. This contradicts the given statement that $m\angle 2 + m\angle 3 \neq 180$.
Step 3: Since the assumption leads to a contradiction, the statement $a \parallel b$ must be false. Therefore, $a \nparallel b$ must be true.

5. **PHYSICS** Sound travels through air at about 344 meters per second when the temperature is 20°C. If Enrique lives 2 kilometers from the fire station and it takes 5 seconds for the sound of the fire station siren to reach him, how can you prove indirectly that it is not 20°C when Enrique hears the siren?

Assume that it is 20°C when Enrique hears the siren, then show that at this temperature it will take more than 5 seconds for the sound of the siren to reach him. Since the assumption is false, you will have proved that it is not 20°C when Enrique hears the siren.

Answers

NAME _____ DATE _____ PERIOD _____

5-3 Enrichment

More Counterexamples

Some statements in mathematics can be proven false by **counterexamples.**
Consider the following statement.

For any numbers a and b, $a - b = b - a$.

You can prove that this statement is false in general if you can find one
example for which the statement is false.

Let $a = 7$ and $b = 3$. Substitute these values in the equation above.

$$7 - 3 \stackrel{?}{=} 3 - 7$$
$$4 \neq -4$$

In general, for any numbers a and b, the statement $a - b = b - a$ is false.
You can make the equivalent verbal statement: subtraction is *not* a
commutative operation.

**In each of the following exercises a, b, and c are any numbers. Prove that
the statement is false by counterexample. Sample answers are given.**

1. $a - (b - c) \stackrel{?}{=} (a - b) - c$

$$6 - (4 - 2) \stackrel{?}{=} (6 - 4) - 2$$
$$6 - 2 \stackrel{?}{=} 2 - 2$$
$$4 \neq 0$$

2. $a \div (b \div c) \stackrel{?}{=} (a \div b) \div c$

$$6 \div (4 \div 2) \stackrel{?}{=} (6 \div 4) \div 2$$
$$\frac{6}{2} \stackrel{?}{=} \frac{1.5}{2}$$
$$3 \neq 0.75$$

3. $a \div b \stackrel{?}{=} b \div a$

$$6 \div 4 \stackrel{?}{=} 4 \div 6$$
$$\frac{3}{2} \stackrel{?}{=} \frac{2}{3}$$

4. $a \div (b + c) \stackrel{?}{=} (a \div b) + (a \div c)$

$$6 \div (4 + 2) \stackrel{?}{=} (6 \div 4) + (6 \div 2)$$
$$6 \div 6 \stackrel{?}{=} 1.5 + 3$$
$$1 \neq 4.5$$

5. $a + (bc) \stackrel{?}{=} (a + b)(a + c)$

$$6 + (4 \cdot 2) \stackrel{?}{=} (6 + 4)(6 + 2)$$
$$6 + 8 \stackrel{?}{=} (10)(8)$$
$$14 \neq 80$$

6. $a^2 + a^2 \stackrel{?}{=} a^4$

$$6^2 + 6^2 \stackrel{?}{=} 6^4$$
$$36 + 36 \stackrel{?}{=} 1296$$
$$72 \neq 1296$$

7. Write the verbal equivalents for Exercises 1, 2, and 3.

1. Subtraction is not an associative operation.
2. Division is not an associative operation.
3. Division is not a commutative operation.

8. For the Distributive Property $a(b + c) = ab + ac$ it is said that multiplication
distributes over addition. Exercises 4 and 5 prove that some operations do not
distribute. Write a statement for each exercise that indicates this.

4. Division does not distribute over addition.
5. Addition does not distribute over multiplication.

NAME _____ DATE _____ PERIOD _____

5-3 Word Problem Practice

Indirect Proof

1. CANOES Thirty-five students went
on a canoeing expedition. They rented
17 canoes for the trip. Use an indirect
proof to show that at least one canoe
had more than two students in it.
**Sample answer: Suppose all
canoes had ≤2 students, then
the total would be less than
or equal to 17 × 2 = 34, a
contradiction.**

2. AREA The area of the United States is
about 6,000,000 square miles. The area
of Hawaii is about 11,000 square miles.
Use an indirect proof to show that at
least one of the fifty states has an area
greater than 120,000 square miles.
**Sample answer: Suppose no
state has area > 120,000 mi².
Then the total area could not
exceed 120,000 × 49 + 11,000 =
5,891,000, a contradiction.**

3. CONSECUTIVE NUMBERS David
was trying to find a common factor
other than 1 between various pairs
of consecutive integers. Write an
indirect proof to show David that
two consecutive integers do not share
a common factor other than 1.
**Sample answer: Let n and $n + 1$
be the consecutive integers.
Suppose they are divisible by the
integer $d > 1$. Then the difference
$n + 1 - n = 1$ is also divisible by
d. But if d divides 1 it cannot be
greater than 1, a contradiction.**

4. WORDS The words *accomplishment,
counterexample,* and *extemporaneous* all
have 14 letters. Use an indirect proof to
show that any word with 14 letters must
use a repeated letter or have two letters
that are consecutive in the alphabet.
**Suppose the letters are distinct
and nonconsecutive. Then the
alphabet must have at least 14 +
13 or 27 letters, a contradiction.**

**LATTICE TRIANGLES For Exercises 5
and 6, use the following information.**
A *lattice point* is a point whose coordinates
are both integers. A *lattice triangle* is a
triangle whose vertices are lattice points. It
is a fact that a lattice triangle has an area
of at least 0.5 square units.

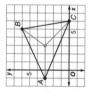

5. Suppose $\triangle ABC$ has a lattice point in its
interior. Show that the lattice triangle
can be partitioned into three smaller
lattice triangles.
Sample answer in diagram above.

6. Prove indirectly that a lattice triangle
with area 0.5 square units contains no
lattice point. (Being on the boundary
does not count as inside.)
**Sample answer: From Exercise 5,
the lattice triangle contains 3
smaller lattice triangles, each
of which has area at least 0.5
square units. The original would
then have area at least 1.5 square
units, a contradiction.**

5-4 Study Guide and Intervention

NAME _____ DATE _____ PERIOD _____

The Triangle Inequality

The Triangle Inequality If you take three straws of lengths 8 inches, 5 inches, and 1 inch and try to make a triangle with them, you will find that it is not possible. This illustrates the Triangle Inequality Theorem.

Triangle Inequality Theorem	The sum of the lengths of any two sides of a triangle is greater than the length of the third side.

Example The measures of two sides of a triangle are 5 and 8. Find a range for the length of the third side.

By the Triangle Inequality, all three of the following inequalities must be true.

$$5 + x > 8 \qquad 8 + x > 5 \qquad 5 + 8 > x$$
$$x > 3 \qquad x > -3 \qquad 13 > x$$

Therefore x must be between 3 and 13.

Exercises

Determine whether the given measures can be the lengths of the sides of a triangle. Write *yes* or *no*.

1. 3, 4, 6   yes

2. 6, 9, 15   no

3. 8, 8, 8   yes

4. 2, 4, 5   yes

5. 4, 8, 16   no

6. 1.5, 2.5, 3   yes

Find the range for the measure of the third side given the measures of two sides.

7. 1 and 6 $5 < n < 7$

8. 12 and 18 $6 < n < 30$

9. 1.5 and 5.5 $4 < n < 7$

10. 82 and 8 $74 < n < 90$

11. Suppose you have three different positive numbers arranged in order from least to greatest. What single comparison will let you see if the numbers can be the lengths of the sides of a triangle?
Find the sum of the two smaller numbers. If that sum is greater than the largest number, then the three numbers can be the lengths of the sides of a triangle.

5-4 Lesson Reading Guide

NAME _____ DATE _____ PERIOD _____

The Triangle Inequality

Get Ready for the Lesson

Read the introduction to Lesson 5-4 in your textbook.

If you assume that non-stop flights go directly to their destination, why will it take longer to get to Albuquerque from any city if you take two flights rather than one?
The flight paths will form a triangle, and the sum of the length of the two non-direct flight paths will be longer than the direct flight paths.

Read the Lesson

1. Refer to the figure.

Which statements are true? **C, D, F**

A. $DE > EF + FD$ B. $DE = EF + FD$

C. $EG = EF + FG$ D. $ED + DG > EG$

E. The shortest distance from D to $\overline{EG}$ is DF.

F. The shortest distance from D to $\overline{EG}$ is DG.

2. Complete each sentence about $\triangle XYZ$.

a. If $XY = 8$ and $YZ = 11$, then the range of values for XZ is __3__ $< XZ <$ __19__.

b. If $XY = 13$ and $XZ = 25$, then YZ must be between __12__ and __38__.

c. If $\triangle XYZ$ is isosceles with $\angle Z$ as the vertex angle, and $XZ = 8.5$, then the range of values for XY is __0__ $< XY <$ __17__.

d. If $XZ = a$ and $YZ = b$, with $b > a$, then the range for XY is __$a - b$__ $< XY <$ __$a + b$__.

Remember What You Learned

3. A good way to remember a new theorem is to state it informally in different words. How could you restate the Triangle Inequality Theorem?
Sample answer: The side that connects one vertex of a triangle to another is a shorter path between the two vertices than the path that goes through the third vertex.

Answers (Lesson 5–4)

Skills Practice (page 31)

5-4 Skills Practice

The Triangle Inequality

Determine whether the given measures can be the lengths of the sides of a triangle. Write *yes* or *no*.

1. 2, 3, 4 yes

2. 5, 7, 9 yes

3. 4, 8, 11 yes

4. 13, 13, 26 no

5. 9, 10, 20 no

6. 15, 17, 19 yes

7. 14, 17, 31 no

8. 6, 7, 12 yes

Find the range for the measure of the third side of a triangle given the measures of two sides.

9. 5 and 9
$4 < n < 14$

10. 7 and 14
$7 < n < 21$

11. 8 and 13
$5 < n < 21$

12. 10 and 12
$2 < n < 22$

13. 12 and 15
$3 < n < 27$

14. 15 and 27
$12 < n < 42$

15. 17 and 28
$11 < n < 45$

16. 18 and 22
$4 < n < 40$

ALGEBRA Determine whether the given coordinates are the vertices of a triangle. Explain.

17. $A(3, 5)$, $B(4, 7)$, $C(7, 6)$
Yes; $AB = \sqrt{5}$, $BC = \sqrt{10}$, and $AC = \sqrt{17}$, so $AB + BC > AC$, $AB + AC > BC$, and $AC + BC > AB$.

18. $S(6, 5)$, $T(8, 3)$, $U(12, -1)$
No; $ST = 2\sqrt{2}$, $TU = 4\sqrt{2}$, and $SU = 6\sqrt{2}$, so $ST + TU = SU$.

19. $H(-8, 4)$, $I(-4, 2)$, $J(4, -2)$
No; $HI = 2\sqrt{5}$, $IJ = 4\sqrt{5}$, and $HJ = 6\sqrt{5}$, so $HI + IJ = HJ$.

20. $D(1, -5)$, $E(-3, 0)$, $F(-1, 0)$
Yes; $DE = \sqrt{41}$, $EF = 2$, and $DF = \sqrt{29}$, so $DE + EF > DF$, $DE + DF > EF$, and $DF + EF > DE$.

Study Guide and Intervention (page 30)

5-4 Study Guide and Intervention (continued)

The Triangle Inequality

Distance Between a Point and a Line

The perpendicular segment from a point to a line is the shortest segment from the point to the line.

The perpendicular segment from a point to a plane is the shortest segment from the point to the plane.

$\overline{PC}$ is the shortest segment from P to $\overline{AB}$.

$\overline{QT}$ is the shortest segment from Q to plane $\mathcal{X}$.

Example Given: Point P is equidistant from the sides of an angle. Prove: $\overline{BA} \cong \overline{CA}$

Proof:

1. Draw $\overline{BP}$ and $\overline{CP} \perp$ to the sides of $\angle RAS$.
2. $\angle PBA$ and $\angle PCA$ are right angles.
3. $\triangle ABP$ and $\triangle ACP$ are right triangles.
4. $\angle PBA \cong \angle PCA$
5. P is equidistant from the sides of $\angle RAS$.
6. $\overline{BP} \cong \overline{CP}$
7. $\overline{AP} \cong \overline{AP}$
8. $\triangle ABP \cong \triangle ACP$
9. $\overline{BA} \cong \overline{CA}$

1. Dist. is measured along a $\perp$.
2. Def. of $\perp$ lines
3. Def. of rt. $\triangle$
4. Rt. angles are $\cong$.
5. Given
6. Def. of equidistant
7. Reflexive Property
8. HL
9. CPCTC

Exercises

Complete the proof.

Given: $\triangle ABC \cong \triangle RST$; $\angle D \cong \angle U$
Prove: $\overline{AD} \cong \overline{RU}$

Proof:

1. $\triangle ABC \cong \triangle RST$; $\angle D \cong \angle U$
2. $\overline{AC} \cong \overline{RT}$
3. $\angle ACB \cong \angle RTS$
4. $\angle ACB$ and $\angle ACD$ are a linear pair; $\angle RTS$ and $\angle RTU$ are a linear pair.
5. $\angle ACB$ and $\angle ACD$ are supplementary; $\angle RTS$ and $\angle RTU$ are supplementary.
6. $\angle ACD \cong \angle RTU$
7. $\triangle ADC \cong \triangle RUT$
8. $\overline{AD} \cong \overline{RU}$

1. Given
2. CPCTC
3. CPCTC
4. Def. of linear pair
5. Linear pairs are suppl.
6. Angles suppl. to $\cong$ angles are $\cong$.
7. AAS
8. CPCTC

NAME _____ DATE _____ PERIOD _____

5-4 Practice

The Triangle Inequality

Determine whether the given measures can be the lengths of the sides of a triangle. Write yes or no.

1. 9, 12, 18 yes

2. 8, 9, 17 no

3. 14, 14, 19 yes

4. 23, 26, 50 no

5. 32, 41, 63 yes

6. 2.7, 3.1, 4.3 yes

7. 0.7, 1.4, 2.1 no

8. 12.3, 13.9, 25.2 yes

Find the range for the measure of the third side of a triangle given the measures of two sides.

9. 6 and 19

$13 < n < 25$

10. 7 and 29

$22 < n < 36$

11. 13 and 27

$14 < n < 40$

12. 18 and 23

$5 < n < 41$

13. 25 and 38

$13 < n < 63$

14. 31 and 39

$8 < n < 70$

15. 42 and 6

$36 < n < 48$

16. 54 and 7

$47 < n < 61$

ALGEBRA Determine whether the given coordinates are the vertices of a triangle. Explain.

17. $R(1, 3)$, $S(4, 0)$, $T(10, -6)$

No; $RS = 3\sqrt{2}$, $ST = 6\sqrt{2}$, and $RT = 9\sqrt{2}$, so $RS + ST = RT$.

18. $W(2, 6)$, $X(1, 6)$, $Y(4, 2)$

Yes; $WX = 1$, $XY = 5$, and $WY = 2\sqrt{5}$, so $WX + XY > WY$, $WX + WY > XY$, and $WY + XY > WX$.

19. $P(-3, 2)$, $L(1, 1)$, $M(9, -1)$

No; $PL = \sqrt{17}$, $LM = 2\sqrt{17}$, and $PM = 3\sqrt{17}$, so $PL + LM = PM$.

20. $B(1, 1)$, $C(6, 5)$, $D(4, -1)$

Yes; $BC = \sqrt{41}$, $CD = 2\sqrt{10}$, and $BD = \sqrt{13}$, so $BC + CD > BD$, $BC + BD > CD$, and $BD + CD > BC$.

21. **GARDENING** Ha Poong has 4 lengths of wood from which he plans to make a border for a triangular-shaped herb garden. The lengths of the wood borders are 8 inches, 10 inches, 12 inches, and 18 inches. How many different triangular borders can Ha Poong make? 3

NAME _____ DATE _____ PERIOD _____

5-4 Word Problem Practice

The Triangle Inequality

1. **STICKS** Jamila has 5 sticks of lengths 2, 4, 6, 8, and 10 inches. Using three sticks at a time as the sides of triangles, how many triangles can she make? 3

Use the figure at the right for Exercises 2 and 3.

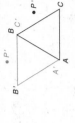

2. **PATHS** To get to the nearest supermarket, Tanya must walk over a railroad track. There are two places where she can cross the track (points A and B). Which path is longer? Explain.

By the triangle inequality, the distance from Tanya's home to point B and on to the supermarket is greater than the straight distance from Tanya's home to the Supermarket.

3. **PATHS** While out walking one day Tanya finds a third place to cross the railroad tracks. Show that the path through point C is longer than the path through point B.

Sample answer: Let S be the supermarket and T be Tanya's home. Because $\angle SAB$ is $90°$, $m\angle SBA < 90°$, so $m\angle SBC > 90°$, making $SC > SB$. Similarly, $CT > BT$. Therefore $CT + CS > BT + BS$.

4. **CITIES** The distance between New York City and Boston is 187 miles and the distance between New York City and Hartford is 97 miles. Hartford, Boston, and New York City form a triangle on a map. What must the distance between Boston and Hartford be greater than? 90 mi

TRIANGLES For Exercises 5–7, use the following information.

The figure shows an equilateral triangle ABC and a point P outside the triangle.

5. Draw the figure that is the result of turning the original figure 60° counterclockwise about A. Denote by P', the image of P under this turn. See figure.

6. Note that $\overline{P'B}$ is congruent to $\overline{PC}$. It is also true that $\overline{PP'}$ is congruent to $\overline{PA}$. Why?

Sample answer: PA is congruent to $P'A$ and $m\angle PAP'$ is $60°$, so by SAS, triangle $PP'A$ is equilateral. Thus, $PP' = PA$.

7. Show that PA, PB, and PC satisfy the triangle inequalities.

Sample answer: $\triangle P'PB$ is a triangle with side lengths equal to PA, PB, and PC.

Answers (Lessons 5–4 and 5–5)

NAME _____ DATE _____ PERIOD _____

5-5 Lesson Reading Guide

Inequalities Involving Two Triangles

Get Ready for the Lesson

Read the introduction to Lesson 5-5 in your textbook.

Suppose the thrill ride starts from the lowest position, rises to its highest position to the left, and then falls back to its lowest position. How many times will the arm make an angle of 20° with the vertical base? **2 times**

Read the Lesson

1. Refer to the figure. Write a conclusion that you can draw from the given information. Then name the theorem that justifies your conclusion.

a. $\overline{LM} \cong \overline{OP}, \overline{MN} \cong \overline{PQ}$, and $LN > OQ$
$m\angle M > m\angle P$; SSS Inequality Theorem

b. $\overline{LM} \cong \overline{OP}, \overline{MN} \cong \overline{PQ}$, and $m\angle P < m\angle M$
$OQ < LN$ (or $LN > OQ$); SAS Inequality Theorem (or Hinge Theorem)

c. $LM = 8, LN = 15, OP = 8, OQ = 15, m\angle L = 22$, and $m\angle O = 21$
$MN > PQ$; SAS Inequality Theorem (or Hinge Theorem)

2. In the figure, $\triangle EFG$ is isosceles with base $\overline{FG}$ and F is the midpoint of $\overline{DG}$. Determine whether each of the following is a valid conclusion that you can draw based on the given information. (Write *valid* or *invalid*.) If the conclusion is valid, identify the definition, property, postulate, or theorem that supports it.

a. $\angle 3 \cong \angle 4$ valid; Isosceles Triangle Theorem

b. $DF = GF$ valid; definition of midpoint

c. $\triangle DEF$ is isosceles. invalid

d. $m\angle 3 > m\angle 1$ valid; Exterior Angle Inequality Theorem

e. $m\angle 2 > m\angle 4$ valid; Exterior Angle Inequality Theorem

f. $m\angle 2 > m\angle 3$ valid; Substitution Property (using conclusions from parts a and e)

g. $DE > EG$ valid; SAS Inequality Theorem (or Hinge Theorem)

h. $DE > FG$ invalid

Remember What You Learned

3. A good way to remember something is to think of it in concrete terms. How can you illustrate the Hinge Theorem with everyday objects? **Sample answer: Put two pencils on a desktop so that the erasers touch. As you increase or decrease the measure of the angle formed by the pencils, the distance between the points of the pencils increases or decreases accordingly.**

Chapter 5   **35**   Glencoe Geometry

NAME _____ DATE _____ PERIOD _____

5-4 Enrichment

Constructing Triangles

The measurements of the sides of a triangle are given. If a triangle having sides with these measurements is not possible, then write *impossible*. If a triangle is possible, draw it and measure each angle with a protractor.

1. $AR = 5$ cm $m\angle A = 30$
$RT = 3$ cm $m\angle R = 94$
$AT = 6$ cm $m\angle T = 56$

2. $PI = 8$ cm $m\angle P =$
$IN = 3$ cm $m\angle I =$
$PN = 2$ cm $m\angle N =$
impossible

3. $ON = 10$ cm $m\angle O =$
$NE = 5.3$ cm $m\angle N =$
$OE = 4.6$ cm $m\angle E =$
impossible

4. $TW = 6$ cm $m\angle T = 112$
$WO = 7$ cm $m\angle W = 15$
$TO = 2$ cm $m\angle O = 53$

5. $BA = 3.1$ cm $m\angle B = 162$
$AT = 8$ cm $m\angle A = 11$
$BT = 5$ cm $m\angle T = 7$

6. $AR = 4$ cm $m\angle A = 90$
$RM = 5$ cm $m\angle R = 37$
$AM = 3$ cm $m\angle M = 53$

Chapter 5   **34**   Glencoe Geometry

5-5 Study Guide and Intervention
Inequalities Involving Two Triangles

SAS Inequality The following theorem involves the relationship between the sides of two triangles and an angle in each triangle.

| SAS Inequality/Hinge Theorem | If two sides of a triangle are congruent to two sides of another triangle and the included angle in one triangle has a greater measure than the included angle in the other, then the third side of the first triangle is longer than the third side of the second triangle. | If $RS \cong AB$, $ST \cong BC$, and $m\angle S > m\angle B$, then $RT > AC$. |

Example Write an inequality relating the lengths of $\overline{CD}$ and $\overline{AD}$.

Two sides of $\triangle BCD$ are congruent to two sides of $\triangle ABD$ and $m\angle CBD > m\angle ABD$. By the SAS Inequality/Hinge Theorem, $CD > AD$.

Exercises

Write an inequality relating the given pair of segment measures.

1. MR, RP
   MR > RP

2. AD, CD
   AD > CD

3. EG, HK
   EG < HK

4. MR, PR
   MR > PR

Write an inequality to describe the possible values of x.

5. x > 12.5

6. x > 1.6

5-5 Study Guide and Intervention (continued)
Inequalities Involving Two Triangles

SSS Inequality The converse of the Hinge Theorem is also useful when two triangles have two pairs of congruent sides.

| SSS Inequality | If two sides of a triangle are congruent to two sides of another triangle and the third side in one triangle is longer than the third side in the other, then the angle between the pair of congruent sides in the first triangle is greater than the corresponding angle in the second triangle. | If $NM = SR$, $MP = RT$, and $NP > ST$, then $m\angle M > m\angle R$. |

Example Write an inequality relating the measures of $\angle ABD$ and $\angle CBD$.

Two sides of $\triangle ABD$ are congruent to two sides of $\triangle CBD$, and $AD > CD$. By the SSS Inequality, $m\angle ABD > m\angle CBD$.

Exercises

Write an inequality relating the given pair of angle measures.

1. $m\angle MPR$, $m\angle NPR$
   $m\angle MPR > m\angle NPR$

2. $m\angle ABD$, $m\angle CBD$
   $m\angle ABD < m\angle CBD$

3. $m\angle C$, $m\angle Z$
   $m\angle C < m\angle Z$

4. $m\angle XYW$, $m\angle WYZ$
   $m\angle XYW < m\angle WYZ$

Write an inequality to describe the possible values of x.

5. 12 < x < 116

6. 1 < x < 12

5-5 Practice

Inequalities Involving Two Triangles

Write an inequality relating the given pair of angles or segment measures.

1. AB, BK

$AB > BK$

2. ST, SR

$ST > SR$

3. $m\angle CDF$, $m\angle EDF$

$m\angle CDF < m\angle EDF$

4. $m\angle R$, $m\angle T$

$m\angle R < m\angle T$

5. Write a two-column proof.
Given: G is the midpoint of $\overline{DF}$.
Prove: $ED > EF$
Proof:

Statements	Reasons
1. G is the midpoint of $\overline{DF}$.	1. Given
2. $\overline{DG} \cong \overline{FG}$	2. Definition of midpoint
3. $\overline{EG} \cong \overline{EG}$	3. Reflexive Property
4. $m\angle 1 > m\angle 2$	4. Given
5. $ED > EF$	5. SAS Inequality

6. TOOLS Rebecca used a spring clamp to hold together a chair leg she repaired with wood glue. When she opened the clamp, she noticed that the angle between the handles of the clamp decreased as the distance between the handles of the clamp decreased. At the same time, the distance between the gripping ends of the clamp increased. When she released the handles, the distance between the gripping end of the clamp decreased and the distance between the handles increased. Is the clamp an example of the SAS or SSS Inequality?
SAS Inequality

5-5 Skills Practice

Inequalities Involving Two Triangles

Write an inequality relating the given pair of angles or segment measures.

1. $m\angle BXA$, $m\angle DXA$

$m\angle BXA < m\angle DXA$

2. BC, DC

$BC > DC$

Write an inequality relating the given pair of angles or segment measures.

3. $m\angle STR$, $m\angle TRU$

$m\angle STR > m\angle TRU$

4. PQ, RQ

$PQ > RQ$

5. In the figure, $\overline{BA}$, $\overline{BD}$, $\overline{BC}$, and $\overline{BE}$ are congruent and $AC < DE$. How does $m\angle 1$ compare with $m\angle 3$? Explain your thinking.
$m\angle 1 < m\angle 3$; From the given information and the SSS Inequality Theorem, it follows that in $\triangle ABC$ and $\triangle DBE$ we have $m\angle ABC < m\angle DBE$. Since $m\angle ABC = m\angle 1 + m\angle 2$ and $m\angle DBE = m\angle 3 + m\angle 2$, it follows that $m\angle 1 + m\angle 2 < m\angle 3 + m\angle 2$. Subtract $m\angle 2$ from each side of the last inequality to get $m\angle 1 < m\angle 3$.

6. Write a two-column proof.
Given: $\overline{BA} \cong \overline{DA}$
$BC > DC$
Prove: $m\angle 1 > m\angle 2$
Proof:

Statements	Reasons
1. $\overline{BA} \cong \overline{DA}$	1. Given
2. $BC > DC$	2. Given
3. $\overline{AC} \cong \overline{AC}$	3. Reflexive Property
4. $m\angle 1 > m\angle 2$	4. SSS Inequality

5-5 Enrichment

NAME _____ DATE _____ PERIOD _____

Hinge Theorem

The Hinge Theorem that you studied in this section states that if two sides of a triangle are congruent to two sides of another triangle and the included angle and the included angle in one triangle has a greater measure than the included angle in the other, then the third side of the first triangle is longer than the third side of the second triangle. In this activity, you will investigate whether the converse, inverse and contrapositive of the Hinge Theorem are also true.

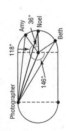

Hypothesis: $XY = QR$, $YZ = RS$, $m\angle 1 > m\angle 2$
Conclusion: $XZ > QS$

1. What is the converse of the Hinge Theorem?
If two sides of one triangle are congruent to two sides of another triangle, and the third side of the first is longer than the third side of the second, then the included angle of the first is larger than the included angle of the second.

2. Can you find any counterexamples to prove that the converse is false?
No, it appears to be true.

3. What is the inverse of the Hinge Theorem?
If two sides of a triangle are *not* congruent to two sides of another triangle *or* the included angle in one triangle *does not have a* greater measure than the included angle in the other, then the third side of the first triangle is *not* longer than the third side of the second triangle.

4. Can you find any counterexamples to prove that the inverse is false?
No, it appears to be true.

5. What is the contrapositive of the Hinge Theorem?
If the third side of the first triangle is *not* longer than the 3rd side of the 2nd, then the other two sides are *not* congruent *or* the included angle *does not have a* greater measure.

6. Can you find any counterexamples to prove that the contrapositive is false?
No, it appears to be true.

Chapter 5   41   Glencoe Geometry

5-5 Word Problem Practice

Inequalities Involving Two Triangles

NAME _____ DATE _____ PERIOD _____

1. **CLOCKS** The minute hand of a grandfather clock is 3 feet long and the hour hand is 2 feet long. Is the distance between their ends greater at 3:00 or at 8:00?
8:00

2. **FERRIS WHEEL** A Ferris wheel has carriages located at the 10 vertices of a regular decagon.

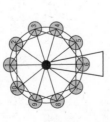

Which carriages are farther away from carriage number 1 than carriage number 4?
5, 6, and 7

3. **WALKWAY** Tyree wants to make two slightly different triangles for his walkway. He has three pieces of wood to construct the frame of his triangles. After Tyree makes the first concrete triangle, he adjusts two sides of the triangle so that the angle they create is smaller than the angle in the first triangle. Explain how this changes the triangle.
Sample answer: By the SAS Inequality Theorem, the third side opposite the angle that was made smaller is now shorter than the third side of the first triangle.

4. **MOUNTAIN PEAKS** Emily lives the same distance from three mountain peaks: High Point, Topper, and Cloud Nine. For a photography class, Emily must take a photograph from her house that shows two of the mountain peaks. Which two peaks would she have the best chance of capturing in one image?

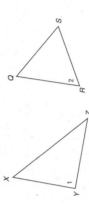

Topper and Cloud Nine

RUNNERS For Exercises 5 and 6, use the following information.
A photographer is taking pictures of three track stars, Amy, Noel, and Beth. The photographer stands on a track, which is shaped like a rectangle with semicircles on both ends.

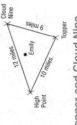

5. Based on the information in the figure, list the runners in order from nearest to farthest from the photographer.
Amy, Beth, Noel

6. Explain how to locate the point along the semicircular curve that the runners are on that is farthest away from the photographer.
Extend the line through the photographer and the center of the semicircle to where it intersects the semicircular track.

Chapter 5   40   Glencoe Geometry

Chapter 5 Assessment Answer Key

Quiz 1 *(Lessons 5–1 and 5–2)*
Page 45

1. circumcenter
2. $\angle 4$
3. centroid
4. $x = -1$
5. $\overline{PQ}$

Quiz 2 *(Lesson 5–3)*
Page 45

1. The conclusion is false.
2. $x \neq 6$
3. $\overline{AB} \not\cong \overline{BC}$
4. Assume that $x \not> 10$. That is, assume that $x \leq 10$.
5. $\overline{CB} \cong \overline{CA}$

Quiz 3 *(Lesson 5–4)*
Page 46

1. $AC < AB < AD$
2. Yes; $AB + AC > BC$, $BC + AC > AB$, and $AB + BC > AC$.
3. AE
4. $2 < x < 16$
5. C

Quiz 4 *(Lesson 5–5)*
Page 46

1. $m\angle 1 < m\angle 2$
2. $AB < DE$
3. $GH > 7$
4. $\overline{AE} \cong \overline{AE}$
5. SSS Inequality

Mid-Chapter Test
Page 47

1. C
2. F
3. D
4. G
5. D
6. $180 > x > 50$
7. $x^2 \leq 4$
8. 16 inches
9. $\overline{BD}$ bisects $\angle ABC$.

Chapter 5 Assessment Answer Key

Vocabulary Test
Page 48

1. false, median

2. false, orthocenter

3. circumcenter

4. incenter

5. greater

6. altitude

7. indirect proof

8. circumcenter

9. three or more lines intersecting at a common point

10. segment with endpoints at a vertex and the midpoint of the side opposite to the vertex

Form 1
Page 49

1. A

2. H

3. D

4. G

5. C

6. G

7. A

8. H

9. B

10. G

11. B

Page 50

12. F

13. B

14. G

15. C

16. G

17. A

18. J

19. D

20. F

B: 6, −1

Answers

Chapter 5 Assessment Answer Key

Form 2A
Page 51

Page 52

Page 54

12. __G__

11. __C__

1. __B__

13. __A__

1. __C__

2. __J__

2. __J__

3. __A__

12. __J__

3. __B__

4. __H__

14. __J__

4. __F__

13. __B__

15. __B__

14. __G__

5. __B__

16. __H__

5. __A__

15. __A__

6. __F__

6. __H__

16. __J__

7. __C__

17. __D__

7. __D__

8. __F__

17. __C__

18. __H__

8. __G__

18. __G__

9. __A__

19. __B__

9. __C__

19. __A__

10. __J__

10. __F__

11. __A__

20. __H__

20. __H__

B: _____9, −2_____

B: _____160_____

Chapter 5 Assessment Answer Key

Form 2C
Page 55

1. $\overrightarrow{AD}$

2. $x = 8$; $\overleftrightarrow{AC}$ is the $\perp$ bisector of $\overline{BD}$.

3. 4

4. $\left(\dfrac{16}{3}, \dfrac{22}{3} \right)$

5. 25

6. $2(z + 3) > \dfrac{x}{5}$

7. $\angle I, \angle H, \angle G$

8. $\overline{PQ}, \overline{PR}, \overline{QR}$

9. $\overline{XY}$

10. 4 is not a factor of n.

11. $\overline{AB}$ is not a median.

Page 56

12. $\angle X \cong \angle Z$

13. 13 m $< x <$ 33 m

14. PT

15. 34

16. $EF < GH$

17. $m\angle 1 > m\angle 2$

18. Definition of $\cong$ segments

19. Reflexive Prop.

20. SSS Inequality

B: $y = \dfrac{c - a}{b}x$

Answers

Chapter 5 Assessment Answer Key

Form 2D
Page 57

1. $\overleftrightarrow{LM}$

2. $x = 5$; $\overleftrightarrow{RS}$ is the $\perp$ bisector of $\overline{PQ}$.

3. 8

4. $\left(\dfrac{9}{2}, \dfrac{3}{2}\right)$

5. 20

6. $7z > x - 5$

7. $\angle T, \angle V, \angle U$

8. $\overline{FH}, \overline{GH}, \overline{GF}$

9. $\overline{LM}$

10. n^2 is not an even number.

11. $\overline{AD}$ is not an altitude.

Page 58

12. $\overline{SV} \perp \overline{PQ}$

13. 15 ft $< x <$ 43 ft

14. BE

15. 35

16. $m\angle 1 < m\angle 2$

17. $BC < ED$

18. Midpoint Theorem

19. Reflexive Prop.

20. SAS Inequality

B: $x = \dfrac{1}{2}a$

Chapter 5 Assessment Answer Key

Form 3
Page 59

1. _____15_____

2. _____$\left(\dfrac{38}{13}, -\dfrac{32}{13}\right)$_____

3. _____32_____

4. _____$146 > m\angle L > 0$_____

5. _____$\angle H, \angle I, \angle G$_____

6. _____$\overline{QR}, \overline{PQ}, \overline{PR}$_____

7. _____shortest: $\overline{VY}$;_____
        longest: $\overline{VW}$

8. _____$x \neq 3$_____

9. _____no; $2 + 4 < 8$_____

10. _____The $\angle$ bisectors are_____
         not concurrent.

11. _____$12x - 31 > 3x - 4$;_____
         $x > 3$

Page 60

12. _____140_____

13. _____$\angle B \cong \angle E$_____

14. _____5 in. $< x <$ 53 in._____

15. _____YW_____

16. _____$3x + 10 > x + 20$;_____
         $x > 5$

17. _____Def. of $\cong$ segments_____

18. _____Addition Prop. of_____
         Inequality

19. _____Reflexive Prop._____

20. _____SSS Inequality_____

B: _____$y = \dfrac{d}{c - 2a}x - \dfrac{2ad}{c - 2a}$_____

Answers

Chapter 5 Assessment Answer Key

Score	General Description	Specific Criteria
4	**Superior** A correct solution that is supported by well-developed, accurate explanations	• Shows thorough understanding of the concepts of *bisectors, medians, altitudes, inequalities in triangles, indirect proof, the Triangle Inequality, SAS Inequality, and SSS Inequality.* • Uses appropriate strategies to solve problems. • Computations are correct. • Written explanations are exemplary. • Figures are accurate and appropriate. • Goes beyond requirements of some or all problems.
3	**Satisfactory** A generally correct solution, but may contain minor flaws in reasoning or computation	• Shows an understanding of the concepts of *bisectors, medians, altitudes, inequalities in triangles, indirect proof, the Triangle Inequality, SAS Inequality, and SSS Inequality.* • Uses appropriate strategies to solve problems. • Computations are mostly correct. • Written explanations are effective. • Figures are mostly accurate and appropriate. • Satisfies all requirements of problems.
2	**Nearly Satisfactory** A partially correct interpretation and/or solution to the problem	• Shows an understanding of most of the concepts of *bisectors, medians, altitudes, inequalities in triangles, indirect proof, the Triangle Inequality, SAS Inequality, and SSS Inequality.* • May not use appropriate strategies to solve problems. • Computations are mostly correct. • Written explanations are satisfactory. • Figures are mostly accurate. • Satisfies the requirements of most of the problems.
1	**Nearly Unsatisfactory** A correct solution with no supporting evidence or explanation	• Final computation is correct. • No written explanations or work shown to substantiate the final computation. • Figures may be accurate but lack detail or explanation. • Satisfies minimal requirements of some of the problems.
0	**Unsatisfactory** An incorrect solution indicating no mathematical understanding of the concept or task, or no solution is given	• Shows little or no understanding of most of the concepts of *bisectors, medians, altitudes, inequalities in triangles, indirect proof, the Triangle Inequality, SAS Inequality, and SSS Inequality.* • Does not use appropriate strategies to solve problems. • Computations are incorrect. • Written explanations are unsatisfactory. • Figures are inaccurate or inappropriate. • Does not satisfy requirements of problems. • No answer given.

Chapter 5 Assessment Answer Key

Extended-Response Test, Page 61
Sample Answers

In addition to the scoring rubric found on page A26, the following sample answers may be used as guidance in evaluating open-ended assessment items.

1. As the sticks are pulled apart the angle gets greater and the rubber band will be stretched and become longer. This situation illustrates the SAS Inequality Theorem.

2. Ashley is correct, $\overleftrightarrow{FG}$ and $\overleftrightarrow{JK}$ are 4 inches apart. The shortest distance from a point to a line is the perpendicular distance. Since $\overline{EH}$ is perpendicular to both lines, its measure is the shortest distance from $\overleftrightarrow{FG}$ to $\overleftrightarrow{JK}$.

3. The segment from B to $\overrightarrow{AC}$ could intersect $\overrightarrow{AC}$ in two different points because the length of the segment, 6, is more than the perpendicular distance from B to $\overrightarrow{AC}$, 5, and less than the length of $\overline{AB}$, 10. $\overline{BD}$ can either slant in towards A or out towards C as shown in this figure.

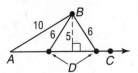

4. **a.** The student should draw a right triangle.

altitudes

b. The student should draw an obtuse triangle.

c. The student should draw an acute triangle.

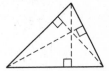

d. The student should draw an equilateral triangle.

Answers

Chapter 5 Assessment Answer Key

Standardized Test Practice

Page 62

1. Ⓐ Ⓑ ● Ⓓ

2. Ⓕ ● Ⓗ Ⓙ

3. Ⓐ Ⓑ ● Ⓓ

4. Ⓕ Ⓖ ● Ⓙ

5. ● Ⓑ Ⓒ Ⓓ

6. ● Ⓖ Ⓗ Ⓙ

7. Ⓐ ● Ⓒ Ⓓ

8. Ⓕ ● Ⓗ Ⓙ

Page 63

9. Ⓐ Ⓑ Ⓒ ●

10. ● Ⓖ Ⓗ Ⓙ

11. Ⓐ ● Ⓒ Ⓓ

12. ● Ⓖ Ⓗ Ⓙ

13. Ⓐ ● Ⓒ Ⓓ

14. Ⓕ Ⓖ Ⓗ ●

15. ● Ⓑ Ⓒ Ⓓ

16.

			8	.			
0	0	0	0		0	0	0
1	1	1	1		1	1	1
2	2	2	2		2	2	2
3	3	3	3		3	3	3
4	4	4	4		4	4	4
5	5	5	5		5	5	5
6	6	6	6		6	6	6
7	7	7	7		7	7	7
8	8	8	●		8	8	8
9	9	9	9		9	9	9

17.

		3	4	.			
0	0	0	0		0	0	0
1	1	1	1		1	1	1
2	2	2	2		2	2	2
3	3	●	3		3	3	3
4	4	4	●		4	4	4
5	5	5	5		5	5	5
6	6	6	6		6	6	6
7	7	7	7		7	7	7
8	8	8	8		8	8	8
9	9	9	9		9	9	9

Chapter 5 Assessment Answer Key

Standardized Test Practice *(continued)*
Page 64

18. _____ 6 _____

19. _____ 10 _____

20. _____ 25 _____

21a. _____ (1, 0) _____

21b. _____ (0, 1) _____

21c. _____ (−2, 3) _____

22a. _____ $y = 5x - 2$ _____

22b. _____ $y = -\dfrac{x}{5} + 2$ _____

22c. _____ $\left(\dfrac{10}{13}, \dfrac{24}{13}\right)$ _____

Answers